Cosmological Clues

Cosmological Clues
Evidence for the Big Bang, Dark Matter and Dark Energy

Carolyn Devereux

CRC Press
Taylor & Francis Group
Boca Raton London New York

CRC Press is an imprint of the
Taylor & Francis Group, an **informa** business

First edition published 2021
by CRC Press
6000 Broken Sound Parkway NW, Suite 300, Boca Raton, FL 33487-2742

and by CRC Press
2 Park Square, Milton Park, Abingdon, Oxon, OX14 4RN

Library of Congress Cataloging-in-Publication Data

Names: Devereux, Carolyn, author.
Title: Cosmological clues : evidence for the big bang, dark matter and dark energy / Carolyn Devereux.
Description: First edition. | Boca Raton, FL : CRC Press, 2020. | Includes bibliographical references and index.
Identifiers: LCCN 2020037694 (print) | LCCN 2020037695 (ebook) | ISBN 9780367407308 (hardback) | ISBN 9780367406943 (paperback) | ISBN 9780367808785 (ebook)
Subjects: LCSH: Cosmology.
Classification: LCC QB981 .D4393 2020 (print) | LCC QB981 (ebook) | DDC 523.1--dc23
LC record available at https://lccn.loc.gov/2020037694
LC ebook record available at https://lccn.loc.gov/2020037695

ISBN: 978-0-367-40730-8 (hbk)
ISBN: 978-0-367-40694-3 (pbk)
ISBN: 978-0-367-80878-5 (ebk)

To all my children
Knowledge changes us

Contents

Preface

It matters to us, as humans, how we see ourselves in the World. We are interested in knowing about where the World came from and that means understanding how the Universe has evolved. Did the Universe have a beginning, will it have an end, or has it always been the same, never changing?

I am a cosmologist working on understanding dark matter and 'weighing' the Universe. The amount of matter in the Universe can tell us whether the Universe will expand forever or collapse back. When I tell people I'm a cosmologist they ask about the Big Bang: 'How do you know the Big Bang happened; what proof is there?' and they want to know about dark matter, 'If we don't know what dark matter is, then have scientists just made it up?' No, we have not just made it up. If you want to know what evidence there is for the existence of the Big Bang, dark matter and dark energy, then read on.

This is the age of precision cosmology. We can build large telescopes, with extremely sensitive detectors, put them into space, and take vast amounts of data using supercomputers to create images. We now have the ability to see galaxies across the whole of the sky and galaxies that are so far away; we are seeing them when they were just forming after the Big Bang. What has made a difference to cosmology as a subject is the use of supercomputers to make computer simulations of how the Universe evolved so that we can test our theories. New observations are being made, new theories are being formed, and new ways of testing our theories are being developed. It is an interesting time to be a cosmologist.

All this leads to rapidly changing ideas with some seeming outlandish, the stuff of science fiction. However, they are based on evidence, mathematics and scientific laws. As weird as multiverses and dark matter may seem there is scientific reasoning behind the concepts. By reading this book you will find out what that reasoning is and about the scientifically accepted model of the evolution of the Universe. You will also gain an understanding of some of the alternative ideas that exist.

Scientific reasoning is the difference between believing something and proving something. It has played an important role in our society. I argue that it is the scientific process that has created our technological society of today and we understand our World better because of it. This book demonstrates the power of the scientific process using cosmology: acquiring evidence, developing a theory and testing the theory with more evidence. Nature is often not what we think it is when we measure it. With impending climate change, it is now even more important than ever that we make decisions based on evidence and continue to test that those decisions are working by gathering more evidence. There seems to be a growing distrust of 'experts' and yet at the same time our society could not exist without experts—experts in treating our water so we can drink it, experts in producing energy and electricity, experts in medicine, experts in making our TVs, computers and internet. Without experts, we cannot live the way we do. Maybe an understanding of the scientific process and the importance of evidence is a way we can bring these two groups of people together.

To highlight the scientific process the book is laid out along the lines of a scientific research paper: Introduction (Chapter 1: The Evolution), Method (Chapter 2: The Reasoning), Results (Chapter 3: The Clues), Interpretation (Chapters 4: The Theories), Discussion (Chapter 5: The Problems), Future Work (Chapter 6: The Testing) and Conclusion (Chapter 7: The Future). Each chapter can be read on its own, although, be aware that the scientific ideas do build on each previous chapter. In the book I often refer to 'we'. By this I do not mean I have done the work; this has been done by many dedicated scientists over centuries. I mean 'we' in the sense of all of us on Earth who now have access to this knowledge.

This book is about the evolution of the Universe, the subject of cosmology. The purpose is to show what evidence exists for how the Universe has evolved and explain what the accepted model of cosmology is: the Big Bang, the expanding Universe, and the existence of dark matter and dark energy. It describes the 'clues' we have from observations and how they have led to this being the accepted model. However, the 'Standard Model of Cosmology' does not explain everything and you will learn where the problems lie, how scientists are working to solve these problems, and some of the key alternative theories that are being worked on to explain the evidence we have, some of which, like 'multiverses', have captured the public's imagination. You do not need a scientific background, only an interest in understanding how the Universe formed, a desire to know more about what evidence there is for the Big Bang, dark matter and dark energy, and a curiosity for how the scientific process has led us to our knowledge of the Universe.

Acknowledgements

I would like to thank the Daphne Jackson Trust for encouraging me to follow my dreams and for giving me the opportunity to explore the wonders of the Universe.

I would also like to thank Professor James Geach and Professor Martin Hardcastle for their academic support and for giving me my first opportunity as a post-doctoral researcher in astrophysics. They took a risk without which I would not have written this book.

I thank my friend Pauline Farrell for the fantastic diagrams she has drawn for the book and the moral support which got me through the difficult bits.

I also thank Kirsten Barr from CRC Press for the much needed encouragement and advice throughout the writing of the book.

Finally, I thank my husband David and my children for their patience, love and the occasional reading of the drafts.

CHAPTER 1

The Evolution

What do we know about the evolution of the universe?
The Scientific Process: INTRODUCTION

> *"Cosmos" comes from Greek meaning harmony or order*
> *"Cosmology" is the study of the evolution of the universe*

1.1 COSMOLOGY – IS THE UNIVERSE EVOLVING?

The universe is a vast and fascinating place. Over the past few thousand years, our view on what makes up the universe has changed and continues to change today. As we improve our technology and build larger telescopes we are seeing new and exciting things that challenge our theories and expands our knowledge. It is an exciting time to be an astronomer looking up at the skies wondering how the universe came to be like it is. What the universe looks like, and how it got to be like it is, is important to us; it affects the way we, as human beings, see ourselves either as tiny specks on a small planet or, as in the past, with us at the centre of everything.

Today, scientists have a view of how the universe has evolved which is based on it beginning with a massive explosion causing the universe to expand; this is the Big Bang. The study of how the universe has evolved, and is evolving, is called cosmology. The current theory includes dark matter, that enabled galaxies to form, and dark energy, which is accelerating the rate at which the universe is expanding. These three things together, the Big Bang, dark matter and dark energy, form the 'Standard Model of Cosmology'. There are three main problems with this model: one, we don't know what caused the Big Bang; two, we don't know what dark matter is; and three, we don't know what dark energy is. So why do scientists have this model? Is it even science or have we just made it up? Well there are clues – observations of the universe – that have led us to this model. We have used the scientific process to develop our ideas, observe the sky to give us evidence, develop a model based on scientific laws to explain the evidence, and then test the model with more evidence. This has led us to our current understanding of how the universe works.

The Cosmological Clues that are explained in this book form the evidence that we have for how the universe works. There are various theories that scientists have developed to explain the Cosmological Clues but none of them, including the Standard Model of Cosmology, explain them all. Cosmology is a subject that requires new ideas to solve the Cosmological Problems making it an interesting and creative field to work in. The imagination required to come up with the theories shows how creative scientists can be. Cosmology really is a place where art and science meets. The concepts of multiverses, time travel, worm holes and black holes are scientific ideas used in films, art and books. Scientists really do create ideas that no-one had imagined before.

It can be hard for those outside of cosmology to know what is an accepted theory by the majority of scientists and what is an outlandish idea proposed by a few. To make it worse for you the reader, it is changing; new evidence is appearing and new ideas are being created. By reading this book you will be better equipped to understand the scientific process and know how to apply it to cosmology so that you can make your own 'scientific' assessment of new theories and observations on the Big Bang, dark matter and dark energy.

1.2   THE STANDARD MODEL OF COSMOLOGY

What is our current model of how the universe evolved?

The Standard Model of Cosmology is made up of three distinct parts that come together to make a unified picture of the way the universe evolved: the hot Big Bang, cold dark matter and dark energy. The standard model is also called the 'Lambda Cold Dark Matter' model represented by ΛCDM. The Λ represents the dark energy and is the symbol for the cosmological constant proposed by Einstein. The CDM stands for cold dark matter. The Big Bang caused the expansion of the universe and is fundamental to the model but has no symbol. There is much observational evidence for the existence of all three elements of the ΛCDM model. However, there is also much we don't know. We don't know what caused the Big Bang and what the universe was at the point of the Big Bang explosion, we don't know what dark matter is, and we don't know what dark energy is.

Not knowing these fundamental things about the model means that it is not complete, there is plenty still to understand. It is not like the Standard Model of particle physics and quantum theory which are highly accurate and well known and research is focused on looking for evidence of where they fail. The ΛCDM model has flaws and gaps, but we use it because it fits a lot of the observations – the Cosmological Clues – and at the present time it is the best model we have. For this reason, it is accepted by the majority of cosmologists as a good working model, one that we can prove or disprove as we get more clues and for this reason it is called the 'concordance model'. An overview of the ΛCDM model is shown in the timeline of Figure 1.1. It shows the evolution of the universe from the Big Bang through to today.

1.2.1 The Big Bang

The Big Bang is an explosion that is considered to be the moment in space and time (shortened to spacetime) that the universe started and resulted in the universe expanding. We don't know what the universe looked like then, or why it exploded, but our model says that it did and that it has been expanding ever since that moment. The Big Bang was extremely hot, it contained all the energy of the universe. In the first millionth of a second after the Big Bang the basic elements and forces that we now see in the universe were formed, producing the sub-atomic particles of electrons, neutrons and protons, along with the strong and weak nuclear forces, gravity, electromagnetism and light. The universe at this stage was a very hot, dense soup of particles and light.

As the universe expanded it cooled down. It is the process of cooling that is the key to the universe evolving and caused the changes that make the universe look like it does today. Between 10 seconds and 20 minutes after the Big Bang, the neutrons and protons cooled enough to combine and form the nuclei of helium which, along with hydrogen, are the lightest elements in the periodic table. In fact, over 98% of visible matter in the universe today is hydrogen and helium. It took a further 380,000 years before the universe had cooled enough for the electrons to combine with the nuclei to form atoms. At this point light stopped hitting the particles and they could move freely through the universe, travelling vast distances, and we can see that light today in what is called the Cosmic Microwave Background (CMB). Further expansion and cooling allowed gravity to pull the atoms together until they were dense enough for nuclear reactions to take place and stars were born giving off heat and light. Over time the stars have been pulled together by gravity to form galaxies (large groupings of stars).

There are three key pieces of evidence that have led to the view that the Big Bang happened:

1. Nearly all galaxies are moving away from us, explained by the universe expanding.

2. The Cosmic Microwave Background has been detected and measured. The best explanation for the CMB is as a consequence of the Big Bang.

3. The measured ratio of hydrogen to helium in the universe is 3:1. The Big Bang, and the particles it produced in the first few minutes, can explain this ratio.

1.2.2 Dark Matter

Dark matter is matter that we cannot see, does not interact with any other types of matter other than by the pull of gravity and we don't know what it

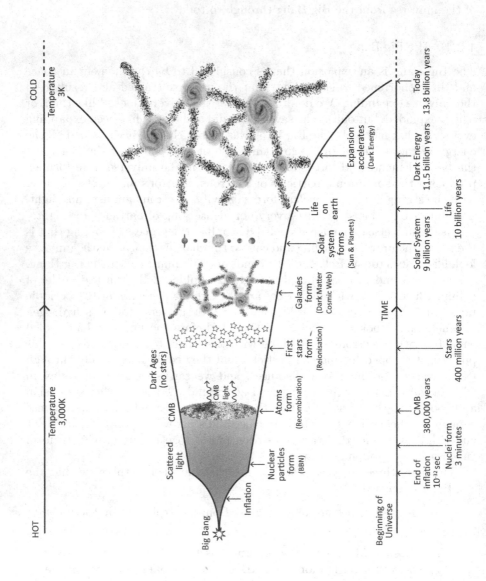

Figure 1.1: Timeline of the universe. The ΛCDM model of the evolution of the universe starting from the Big Bang through to today. Inflation has been added at the beginning although it is not part of the Standard Model of Cosmology. Credit: C. Devereux and P. Farrell.

is. Dark matter makes up 85% of all the matter in the universe and is essential for the formation of stars and galaxies. Dark matter cannot be seen directly. It was first observed, indirectly, by Fritz Zwicky in 1930, when he found that clusters of galaxies were rotating faster on the outside than was expected. In order to explain this, it was necessary to add more matter into the cluster than could be seen from the stars in the cluster – much more matter, in fact about 85% more. As happens sometimes in science, this observation was ignored for 50 years because it was hard to accept that there was that much unknown matter in the universe. But in 1980, Vera Rubin made a similar observation on galaxies and found that the stars on the outside of the galaxies were rotating faster than they should be if they followed the laws of gravity. Once again the existence of dark matter was proposed as the solution to this problem. Now the evidence was getting stronger for dark matter to be there and scientists could not just ignore it, even though there is no theory as to what this dark matter could be.

In the late 20th century, scientists carried out a detailed survey of the observable galaxies across the night sky. When the positions of these galaxies were plotted into a map it was found that there was a structure to where the galaxies lay, it formed filaments and blobs that look like a spider's web. This is called the cosmic web – it is the large-scale structure of the universe. We can use computers to make simulations of this large-scale structure using our knowledge of cosmology and from this see whether we can reproduce the way the cosmic web looks. This has shown us that we can only reproduce what it looks like if we include an extra 85% of matter compared to the matter we see in stars. We have called this unknown matter 'dark matter' and we still do not know what it is. We can't see it and it doesn't interact with 'normal matter' other than by gravity. Reproducing the observed cosmic web using computers is a further piece of evidence that dark matter exists.

We can consider dark matter to be cold or hot. Hot means that it is moving at speeds close to the speed of light, it has high energies, which in physics terms means hot. Cold dark matter moves at slower speeds, not close to the speed of light (although it can still be really fast), it has less energy and we call it cold. By putting cold or hot dark matter into our computer simulations of the cosmic web we find that hot dark matter does not reproduce what we observe but that cold dark matter does. Cold dark matter has become part of the Standard Model of Cosmology.

1.2.3 Dark Energy

Dark energy causes the acceleration of the expansion of the universe. It is not known what dark energy is but the accelerating effect was observed in 1998 when supernovae were found to be moving away from us faster than expected. The evidence for dark energy is sufficient to include it in the Standard Model even though we don't know what it is.

1.2.4 The Cosmological Principle

All physics theories that describe nature must obey the laws of physics, for example, gravity, sub-atomic particle physics, quantum theory. Cosmologists have an extra important principle that any model of cosmology must obey – the 'cosmological principle'. This states that the universe does not have any unique, special place. Wherever you are in the universe, whichever galaxy or star you are looking from, the universe looks the same.

1.3   SCIENTIFIC THINKING

How did we get to the Standard Model of Cosmology?

Humans have always sought to understand the World we live in. All cultures throughout the ages have had a story of how the World was created and as part of that story there is often a deity to look after the World. The belief in these stories, and deities gives hope, an essential requirement for humans. People prayed to the Gods that a storm wouldn't come because they hoped to prevent their crops being destroyed or their houses being turned to rubble. And if a destructive storm came they prayed again so that another one wouldn't come.

And then scientific thinking came along and gave us the knowledge to predict the weather and tell us when a storm is coming so that we can act to limit the damage from the storm. Today, science is telling us that there will be more storms, an increasing number of storms that will be stronger, wilder and more damaging. Science also tells us how we can prevent these storms, by stopping global warming, and for that we can again use science to develop new technologies. Importantly, we can also use scientific thinking to guide our actions, well thought through actions based on evidence. The scientific process has been, and continues to be, important and is the bedrock of our technological age.

Is there something really clever about it? No. It is the process of trial and error, of observing something and trying to explain it, of using evidence rather than belief. The basic scientific process is:

1. to gather some evidence by experiment or observation,

2. to develop a theory that will explain that evidence,

3. to test the theory by gathering more evidence, for example, by using the theory to predict something we can measure and then measuring it to see if it fits the theory.

This is a simple yet powerful 'evidence-based' process of gathering evidence, devising a theory, then testing of the theory with more evidence.

Science is a well tested process that continually develops knowledge. It is the scientific process that we should be precious about not the knowledge itself, that changes as we improve what we know. The true activity of science is working in such an unsure environment; our theories change as we get more evidence. Science is not 'fact', it is accepted knowledge based on the best evidence we have to date. There is an element of art to science, it is a creative process based on knowledge. It is also a process of persuading other scientists that your ideas are right, although sometimes, the loudest voices do not always have the best answers.

So why is cosmology a good topic for understanding the scientific process? In cosmology we have scientific observations, clues, that we cannot fully explain and several different theories exist to understand these clues. There is an accepted view, the 'Standard Model of Cosmology', and although this explains much of the evidence, there are significant unknowns such as what is dark matter, what is dark energy and what was the Big Bang. But the process of observing, making theories and predictions, and then testing those theories is an active one at the moment; the research being done today uses the scientific process and it is easy to see it in action.

1.4 KEY HISTORICAL COSMOLOGICAL CLUES

A brief history of cosmology

1.4.1 ca 350 BC: The Earth at the Centre of the Universe

The geocentric universe

When you look up at the sky, there are clues that tell you how the universe works. The most basic clues can be seen with the naked eye: from the way the Sun, moon, planets and stars move across the sky. This has fascinated people throughout the ages and all cultures have developed stories to provide an explanation of the objects in the sky, how they were created and why they move across the sky.

Astronomy has an ancient history. The earliest known star catalogues are from the Babylonians ca 1200 BC. They recorded eclipses, positions of planets and the moon, and developed the sexagesimal (base 60) number system that is still used today in our division of hours into 60 minutes and circles into 360 degrees. In China and India there are records of astronomical observations from before 500 BC.

The story of Western astronomy starts about 2,500 years ago when the Ancient Greek philosophers began to study the objects in the sky and wrote down what they saw. They looked to understand the movements using mathematical thinking that Pythagoras had developed from his studies of musical intervals and harmonics. Pythagoras became famous for his geometry of right-angled triangles and we continue to learn Pythagoras' theorem in schools today. The Ancient Greeks questioned what they observed and looked for explanations that fitted their observations in a better way than the cultural stories. They developed theories to explain what they saw and they wrote down their thoughts so that others could learn from them.

What are the clues that the Ancient Greeks saw from looking at the sky with the naked eye (the same clues that you can see today)?

- *Clue I of the Ancient Greeks*: The sun moves across the sky every day, rising from the East and setting in the West. The Sun is always a circle shape.

- *Clue II of the Ancient Greeks*: The moon also moves across the sky every day, rising from the East and setting in the West. The moon changes shape over a period of a month, from a circle to a crescent, eventually disappearing and reappearing as a crescent, then growing to a circle again.

- *Clue III of the Ancient Greeks*: When looking at the stars the constellations stay the same relative to each other and they move across the sky during the night, generally going from East to West but also with a diagonal movement depending on where you are on Earth. (If the Ancient Greeks had visited the North or South Pole they would have seen the stars moving in a circle around the pole). The constellations that can be seen also change with the seasons.

- *Clue IV of the Ancient Greeks*: There is no observable parallax of the stars. Parallax is seen when you observe two objects with one further away than the other; when you move positions the gap between the two objects changes. You can see this when you look at trees in the distance while walking, or cover one eye then the other. We now know that this cannot be seen in stars by eye because the distances are so great but we can measure it today with telescopes.

- *Clue V of the Ancient Greeks*: Five planets can be seen by eye: Mercury, Venus, Mars, Jupiter and Saturn. Although planets may look like stars, they differ in that they change position with respect to the stars each night. They also have complicated movements across the sky; they mostly move in one direction but sometimes they move backwards against the background of the stars in what is called 'retrograde' motion.

The Ancient Greeks set about devising a model to explain these clues. There were two key assumptions that influenced the model and continued to dominate for the next 1,800 years:

- *Assumption I of the Ancient Greeks*: Religious beliefs required that the Earth was a divine being and needed to be at the centre of the universe.

- *Assumption II of the Ancient Greeks*: Plato considered that the purest shape was a circle and it was assumed that the movements of astral bodies were on a sphere and with constant speed. Although this sounds logical, it significantly restricted the understanding of the movements of the planets for 2,000 years since they move in ellipses and vary in speed.

In ca 350 BC, it was from these assumptions and clues that Plato proposed that the Sun, moon, stars and planets moved on spheres round the Earth. This view, called the geocentric universe, prevailed throughout the medieval ages. Plato was the leader of the Greek Academy and had been a student of Socrates, considered to be the father of philosophy, and although Socrates did not write down his teachings Plato did, both Socrates teachings and his own. This made him an influential person and his theory was generally accepted. The geocentric universe fitted most of the clues, the main exception being the retrograde movement of the planets. This was the most difficult observation to explain and it took almost 2,000 years before a theory that fitted the planets' motions was developed.

The geocentric view of the universe was also supported by Aristotle, who was a student of Plato and also influential; he tutored Alexander the Great so had the ear of Kings. Aristotle, along with many other ideas, held the view that all objects fall towards the centre of the universe which he based on evidence from another clue.

- *Clue VI of the Ancient Greeks*: When a ball is thrown into the air it falls back to Earth. Aristotle proposed that if the Sun was at the centre of the universe, then the ball would fall towards the Sun (gravity was not known about in Ancient Greece).

However, this was not the only model that was proposed at the time. For example, Heraclides of Pontus, who was also a student of Plato, proposed that the Sun and stars stay still and the Earth moves by rotating on it's axis from west to east every 24 hours. Heraclides was said to have the nickname 'Pomicus', maybe because he was considered to be pompous, and possibly why his theory was not accepted by other philosophers.

Another theory that was ahead of it's time was proposed by Aristarchus in ca 280 BC and stated that the planets, including Earth, went round the Sun. He also thought that the stars were suns a long distance away which was why no parallax was observed. His ideas were not accepted by other philosophers since at that time it was generally accepted that there was no evidence that the Earth moved and to see the parallax of the stars we had to wait until telescopes were invented.

- *Clue VII of the Ancient Greeks*: To prove that the Earth did not move the evidence used was the following: when a ball (or any object) is thrown directly upwards into the air it falls back to the same place, and if the Earth moved then it would fall back to a different place. We now know that the motion of the Earth and the ball (before throwing it in the air) are the same, therefore there is no relative motion between the Earth and the ball, and the movement of the Earth makes no observable affect when the ball is thrown. This is just the same as when you throw a ball on a moving train.

Although Aristarchus' theory was not taken up in 280 BC, it was taken up 1,800 years later by Copernicus who read his theory and used it to develop the heliocentric universe that revolutionised astronomy.

It is interesting to note that the situation in the times of the Ancient Greeks has similarities to that in cosmology today. There are observations for which there is no single model that fits all the evidence therefore many models are proposed but one model is more accepted than the others; in Ancient Greece it was the geocentric universe and today it is the Standard Model of Cosmology. It does not mean that this model is the 'correct' one, it just means that more of the clues fit this model than the others. It also means that it fits more of the assumptions and beliefs that are made by the scientists at that time. Stating the assumptions that models are based on is something scientists have to be very clear about and sometimes scientists have to take the difficult path of changing those assumptions; we shall have an example of this when we discuss Galileo.

In ca 130 BC another clue was discovered. Hipparchus of Nicaea, considered to be one of the greatest ancient astronomical observers and also considered to be the father of trigonometry, catalogued the positions and brightness of 850 stars. His method of assigning brightness is the basis of our 'apparent magnitude' system today. This in itself was a great feat, but he went on to do something even greater. He compared the positions he measured with that of Timocharis that were recorded 150 years earlier. When he did this he found that there was a slight 'wobble' in the movement of the stars. This was another clue.

- *Clue VIII of the Ancient Greeks*: Throughout the year, the positions of the constellations of the stars change slightly.

Today, we call this the 'precession of the equinoxes' and is the Earth's axis changing direction (precessing). The Earth is not perfectly spherical (it is a squashed sphere, called an oblate spheroid) and the gravitational influence of the Sun and moon on the bulge at the equator causes the precession. A single rotation of the precession takes 25,772 years, so for Hipparchus to have found it was truly amazing.

Three-hundred years later in 133 AD, the philosopher and astronomer Ptolemy modified the geocentric universe in 13 volumes called the '*Almagest*'. He recorded his model in a catalogue of the stars, tables that could be used to predict past and future positions of the planets, and bought together much of astronomical knowledge at that time, including the work of Hipparchus. It became the authoritative book on astronomy. Ptolemy tracked and recorded the movement of Saturn across the sky and recorded that it sometimes moved

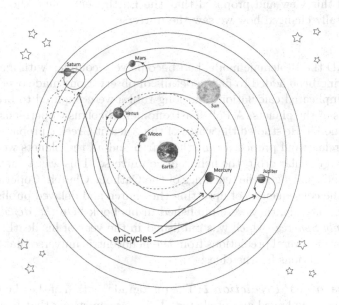

Figure 1.2: The Ptolemaic universe. The Earth is at the centre of the universe with the Sun, moon and five planets orbiting it. The planets have epicycles added to their orbits to correct for their retrograde motion. Credit: P. Farrell.

backwards. Rather than develop a new model, Ptolemy amended the geocentric universe by adding extra circles of movement (epicycles) that the planets make Ptolemy's universe is shown in Figure 1.2. As future astronomers made more observations, the discrepancies in the model increased and extra circles were added until the model was extremely complicated but was quite good at predicting astral movements, though the retrograde movement of the planets remained an issue.

Since Plato's geocentric theory, the model of the universe has changed as more evidence was gathered. In particular, there have been a few key moments in history that have radically changed how we see the Earth within the universe. These paradigm shifts were a result of important clues that changed our view about the size of the universe and Earth's place in the universe, and in doing so changed the way we see ourselves.

1.4.2   1543: The Earth Rotates Round the Sun

The heliocentric universe

The theory that the Earth was at the centre of everything prevailed until the Renaissance era nearly 500 years ago, when Copernicus and Galileo challenged this view and proposed that the Earth went round the sun. This fundamentally changed how we saw the universe.

Copernicus

By 1500 AD the Ptolemaic model had become very complex with many extra circles having been added to fit the details of observations made over the centuries. Complicated calculations and long tables were required to predict the movements of the planets. A Polish astronomer, Nicolaus Copernicus, wanted a simpler model. He studied the works of the Ancient Greeks, probably including Aristarchus, and proposed that the Earth and all the planets went round the Sun in a circular orbit, the heliocentric universe. This was a controversial proposal and challenged the teachings of the Catholic Church. Copernicus was fearful of the consequences of upsetting the church and delayed publishing his theories. Eventually, they were published in his book "*On the Revolutions of the Heavenly Spheres*" which was published in the year of his death, 1543.

There were several predictions from the heliocentric universe that provided simpler explanations for the clues:

- *Copernicus' Prediction I*: The retrograde motion of the planets could be easily explained and predicted. This was something that had plagued the geocentric universe.

- *Copernicus' Prediction II*: It established the order of the planets. Mercury and Venus orbit between the Sun and Earth, with Mercury closest to the Sun, so that only these two planets can be seen 'transiting' across the surface of the Sun. Mars, Jupiter and Saturn are further from the Sun than Earth, with Mars closest to Earth and Saturn furthest away, and can be seen at 180 degrees from the Sun.

- *Copernicus' Prediction III*: The stars must be at a significantly greater distance than had previously been thought because no parallax is seen when the Earth orbits the Sun. The universe became a bigger place.

Despite the simplicity of the model, the predictions of the planetary motions were no more accurate than the complex Ptolemaic model. This was because Copernicus also used circular orbits in his model; the assumptions of the Ancient Greeks, requiring orbits to be a perfect circle shape, were difficult to look beyond. Copernicus also required epicycles to provide a fix to make his model work, this meant that most astronomers, happy with their complicated tables that worked, stuck to the old geocentric universe. It took further observational clues to allow the heliocentric universe to be generally accepted.

Kepler

In 1597, Johannes Kepler from Germany, supported Copernicus' view of the planets moving round the Sun and took the model further. He argued that the

Sun was the origin of the forces holding the planets in the orbits. In studying the orbit of Mars, he showed that it's movement had to be round the Sun, not the Earth. He showed that Mars changed its speed along it's orbit and, in a leap of intuition, he proposed that it swept out equal areas in equal times. This came to be known as Kepler's second law of planetary motion. Kepler then went on to use observations from his teacher Tycho Brahe, an eccentric Danish astronomer who lost his nose in a dual when arguing about who was the best mathematician. Tycho Brache's measurements are considered to be the last great observations by eye and were ten times more accurate than previous astronomers. It is this accuracy that allowed Kepler to develop his laws. Kepler showed that the orbit of Mars was not a circular path but was in fact an ellipse with the Sun at one of the foci of the ellipse. This was another great use of his imagination and became Kepler's first law of planetary motion. Kepler developed a third law relating the time it takes a planet to orbit the Sun (the orbital period) to the distance the planet is from the Sun.

- *Kepler's first law of planetary motion*: The orbit of a planet is an ellipse with the Sun at one of the foci.

- *Kepler's second law of planetary motion*: A planet orbiting the Sun sweeps out equal areas during equal time intervals.

- *Kepler's third law of planetary motion*: The orbital period of a planet round the Sun (squared) is related to the longest axis of it's orbit (cubed).

Kepler used clues from the measurements of Tycho Brahe to develop his important laws but he did not know why the planets moved in this way. The explanation had to wait for the ingenius thinking of Isaac Newton.

Galileo

The next clue came from a technological development – the grinding of glass very finely to make a dome that could produce high quality lenses. This led to the invention of the telescope which is attributed to Hans Lipperhey, a Dutch lens-grinder. For the first time the planets could be seen at a higher magnification than with the naked eye. The famous Italian scientist, Galileo Galilei, was intrigued by the new invention and went about making himself one. In 1609, a month after hearing about the telescope, he had made one three times more powerful than that of Lipperhey (a magnification of nine times), and six months later had a telescope with 33 times the magnification. Galileo looked up at the skies with his new telescope and immediately made significant discoveries which he published in 1610 in his book *'Siderius Nuncias (The Starry Messenger)'*. Some of these discoveries provided important observational evidence for Copernicus' heliocentric universe. These were more clues.

- *Galileo's Clue 1*: The Milky Way, which by eye can be seen as a white cloud of light crossing the night sky, was actually a vast number of stars. This gave evidence for Copernicus' view that the stars were not fixed on a sphere.

- *Galileo's Clue 2*: Jupiter has four moons which can be seen to orbit Jupiter over a period of weeks.

- *Galileo's Clue 3*: Saturn has rings, which Galileo interpreted as moons that were close to Saturn.

- *Galileo's Clue 4*: Venus has phases. It appears circular when it is furthest away from Earth and a crescent shape when it is on the same side of the Sun as Earth. This is easily explained by the Earth and Venus orbiting the Sun whereas the geocentric universe gave the wrong shapes for the phases.

- *Galileo's Clue 5*: The moon has mountains and craters on it, and is not smooth as previously assumed, suggesting that the moon is a similar body to Earth.

As the clues accumulated, the Catholic Church grew uneasy with the challenge to their 'truth' and the geocentric supporting scientists had to rely increasingly on religious arguments to support the model. In 1615, Galileo was tried by the Roman Inquisition on the charge of 'suspicion of heresy' for which he was acquitted if he stopped defending the Copernican view. The Church also issued a decree that it was heretical to state that the Earth moved. Seventeen years later (in 1632), Galileo wrote his great treatise *'Dialogue on the Two Chief World Systems, Ptolemaic and Copernican'*. He wrote it as a dialogue between three speakers which he thought would be acceptable to the church. It was not; he was put on trial for violating his conditions from the previous trial. After being threatened with torture, he publicly rejected the Copernicus view and was kept under house arrest for nine years until his death. When a scientist challenges the accepted norms it can have big personal consequences.

Newton
It took a further 45 years after Galileo's death to find out what caused the planets to rotate round the Sun. In 1687, Sir Isaac Newton published his famous *'Principia Mathematica'* which included his discovery of the force of gravity. This provided the reason for why the Earth and planets orbit the Sun. The findings of Newton are summarised in his three laws of motion and his law of gravity, key laws that are still important today:

- *Newton's law of gravity*: There is an attractive force between two objects which gets stronger as the objects get closer together following an inverse square law. This means that the force gets weaker as the objects move apart related to their distance (squared). The force between two objects is always attractive.

- *Newton's first law of motion*: An object remains in uniform motion (or at rest) unless acted on by an external force.

- *Newton's second law of motion*: The force on an object is equal to it's mass multiplied by it's acceleration.

- *Newton's third law of motion*: Every action has an equal and opposite reaction.

Newton used his laws, along with those of Kepler, to show that the planets orbit the Sun due to the force of gravity. Newton proposed that the force causing the acceleration of objects towards Earth, gravity, is the same as that keeping the moon orbiting the Earth. The moon orbits the Earth by 'falling' towards it, but the forward speed of the moon makes it 'miss' the Earth and therefore rotate about the Earth.

1.4.3   1918: The Sun Rotates Round the Galaxy

The galactocentric universe

Galileo's observation that the Milky Way consisted of many stars was the first clue that the universe was bigger than a fixed sphere. It took over 100 years, into the 1750s, before it was shown that the Sun existed as one star within the many stars making up the Milky Way, and a further 175 years for it to be accepted that the Sun went round the centre of the Milky Way.

The English astronomer, Thomas Wright, was looking for an explanation as to why the Milky Way had a circular distribution across the sky. In 1750, he published *An original theory or new hypothesis of the universe* in which he proposed that the Solar System (the Sun and planets) was part of the Milky Way which was the shape of a flattened disc of stars. Wright also speculated that the faint cloudy patches seen in the sky, called nebulae, are other galaxies that are a great distance away. This built on the observational work of Edmund Halley (of Halley's comet fame) who studied nebulae and suggested that they could be 'light created before the Sun'. The philosopher Immanuel Kant published in 1755 his work on putting these ideas into the mathematical framework of Newton's laws and hypothesised that the nebulae were 'island universes'. More evidence was provided in 1785 by the Herschel siblings, Caroline and William, who counted the number of stars in 683 regions of the sky and concluded that the Milky Way is indeed a disc shaped galaxy that rotated and the Sun is at it's centre. The model remained a heliocentric one, although now the universe was at least the size of the Milky Way, and with the possibility of other galaxies existing, the universe could be much bigger. More evidence was needed.

Over 100 years later, in the early 1900s, the size and shape of the Milky Way was still a topic of debate. Jacobus Kapteyn, a Dutch astronomer, observed the positions and movements of the stars in the Milky Way and estimated that it was an oblate spheroid shape with approximately 8.5 kpc

Figure 1.3: The Milky Way Galaxy. This artist's picture shows what we think the Milky Way looks like. Two major spiral arms can be seen attached to the ends of a thick central bar. *The position of the Sun is shown. Credit: NASA/JPL-Caltech/R. Hurt (SSC/Caltech).

diameter and 2 kpc thick with the Sun at 0.6 kpc from the centre. (A kpc is a kiloparsec, a unit of distance that astronomers use.) This is called the 'Kapteyn universe'. A few years later, in 1918, the American astronomer Harlow Shapley used his observations of pulsating stars (called RR Lyrae) to estimate the distance to globular clusters, which are groups of stars (there are about 150 to 200 in the Milky Way). From this he determined that the Milky Way has a diameter of about 100 kpc and the Sun is at 15 kpc from the centre. This was much bigger than the measurements of Kapteyn and put the Sun away from the centre, meaning that the Sun rotates about the Galaxy. This was evidence for the galactocentric universe. In fact, Kapteyn's estimate was too small and Shapley's was too large. Today, our estimate of the Milky Way is that it has a diameter of 50 kpc and the Sun is 8 kpc from the centre of the Galaxy. It took a few more years for the galactocentric model to be accepted, by about 1925, but it was a short-lived model and was quickly superseded by the work of the great astronomer Edwin Hubble.

1.4.4   1925: The Universe is Infinite with No Centre

The extragalactic universe

The next paradigm shift came from the clue that the Milky Way is not the only galaxy in the universe, there are billions (or possibly trillions) of other galaxies. We call any galaxies that are not the Milky Way 'extragalactic'.

It starts with the American astronomer Henrietta Leavitt who, in 1912 while working as a 'computer' at the Harvard College Observatory, developed a technique to measure greater distances to the stars. Leavitt was working on pulsating stars called Cepheid variables and noticed that the brighter Cepheids took longer to pulse than dimmer ones. She established a relationship between the period of the pulsations and their brightness which allowed Cepheids to be used as what is known as a 'standard candle'. This is now known as Leavitt's Law and allowed astronomers to measure large distances that is still used today. Shapley used Leavitt's discovery for his measurements of the distances to globular clusters to provide evidence for the galactocentric universe.

Another American astronomer, Heber Curtis, was studying nebulae which are clouds of dust and gas. His distance measurements were much larger than those of Shapley's globular clusters, and Curtis proposed that the nebulae were big and far away and exist in other galaxies. Shapley maintained that the nebulae were small and lay in the Milky Way, and concluded that there were no galaxies beyond the Milky Way. The disagreement between the two scientists resulted in what is now called 'The Great Debate'. The debate took place on the 26th April 1920 at the Smithsonian Institute of Natural History. The debate did not come to any conclusion. Again, more clues were needed.

The defining clue came in 1924, by the American astronomer Edwin Hubble. A new 2.5 m diameter telescope, the Hooker Telescope, had just been completed at the Mount Wilson Observatory and was the largest ever built at that time. Hubble was working on this telescope to observe Cepheid variables in nebulae. By using the power of the Hooker Telescope he could improve the accuracy of the measurements of distances to the nebulae. He found that several of the nebulae had significantly greater distances than the size of the Milky Way so they had to exist outside of it. This was the evidence needed that galaxies existed outside of the Milky Way, and the extragalactic view of the universe became accepted when he presented his findings in 1925 to a meeting of the American Astronomical Society. This was a revolutionary observation on a par with Galileo's discoveries when looking through the first telescopes. Hubble's clue led to the view that the universe is infinite and that our Milky Way is not unique.

1.4.5 1932: The Universe Had a Beginning and Evolves

The expanding universe

Discovering galaxies outside of the Milky Way, although important, was not Edwin Hubble's greatest achievement. In 1929, Hubble had what is now considered to be his greatest discovery, he showed that the galaxies are moving away from us and from this he concluded that the universe is expanding. This is called 'Hubble's Law' and is extremely important in modern cosmology.

This was another paradigm shift in our thinking about the universe. Until then, the universe had been assumed to be unchanging; it's always been here and will continue to be here for infinity. Now, Hubble was proposing that the universe is changing, it is expanding. If the universe is expanding going forwards in time then, if we go backwards in time, it must have been contracting until ultimately there was a single point that the universe began from. This is the point at which the Big Bang happened and the universe started. A universe that started from an explosion, from a single point, is called the 'Big Bang Model' and is a key part of the current 'Standard Model of Cosmology'. This was the start of cosmology as a topic in it's own right, because now the universe is seen as changing in time and we can investigate these changes.

Since the universe is expanding, and had a beginning, it may also have an end. Looking into the future to determine how the universe will end is difficult and it depends on the accuracy of our detailed measurements.

There was much debate about the Big Bang model and it was not accepted by all scientists. A key proponent against it was the British astronomer, Fred Hoyle, who supported an unchanging, steady state universe and argued that matter is created between the galaxies allowing new galaxies to form as the universe expands. Hoyle rejected the Big Bang model right up to his death in 2001. Ironically, it was Hoyle who coined the phrase 'The Big Bang' when arguing against it on BBC radio in 1949. The name stuck even though his ideas did not. The general acceptance of the Big Bang model came in 1964 when the Cosmic Microwave Background was observed, providing a clue that the Big Bang model explains very well.

1.4.6 When Did the Standard Model Become Accepted?

With each new set of clues that have been discovered, our understanding of the size of the universe has changed. The Ancient Greeks believed that the stars were fixed on a sphere around the Earth. Then Copernicus showed that the stars must be at a much greater distance away because no parallax is observed when the Earth rotates about the Sun, rapidly followed by Galileo observing that the Milky Way consisted of stars. In 1785, Herschel showed that the Sun is one star within the Galaxy and the size of the universe became at least as big as the Milky Way and maybe there were other 'island universes' making it much bigger. Then in 1924, Hubble ended the Great Debate by providing evidence that other galaxies exist, and the size of the universe was considered to be infinite. In 1929, Hubble went on to provide the clue that the universe was expanding and the size of the universe became finite again. For the first time the universe had an age, the current estimate is 13.8 billion years. Today, we do not know if the universe is infinite or finite, but we consider that the finite size of the universe is the amount we are ever able to see, given that light travels at a fixed speed. The current estimate of the size of the observable universe is 93 billion light-years (9×10^{23} km). (A light-year is the distance light can travel in one year; 9.5 million million kilometres.)

We can see from looking at the history of cosmological theories that changing an accepted theory is a difficult process even when the evidence is there. When a major theory change occurred there has been debate, disagreements, and even threats of torture. We can also see that each theory change required new clues that either came from new technology or from a new way of thinking. It took three decades for Hubble's Big Bang theory of an expanding universe to be accepted by the general population of scientists. It took over 50 years from the first evidence of the existence of dark matter to it being added to the Big Bang model in the 1980s. The development of a standard model took a few more years. In 1995, Jerry Ostriker and Paul Steinhardt [1] published a proposal in the journal *Nature* where they used the phrase the 'concordance model' because it was in accordance with the best cosmological measurements that existed at that time.

In 1998, the discovery of the accelerating expansion of the galaxies provided the evidence for the existence of dark energy and it was accepted as part of the model. The model became known as 'The Standard Model of Cosmology' and is now the leading model, although, as you will see in the rest of this book; it is not the only model and some scientists continue to look for alternative explanations to the clues. If changes to the accepted model are required, it will not be easy and it will be necessary to have new clues.

1.5 WHERE ARE WE IN THE UNIVERSE?

Do we live in a special place in the universe?

Earth does not live in a special place. The cosmological principle tells us that there is no special place in the universe. There is no central point that the whole universe revolves around, there is no unique centre or edge that we can use to define our position in the universe. What we can do is define where we are relative to other objects in the sky, nearby stars and galaxies, just as we can use the constellations of the stars to navigate at sea. The place to start is where the Earth is relative to the Sun.

Earth is a small planet that goes round the Sun in an orbit that is an elliptical shape. At it's closest it is 148 million kilometres from the Sun (in January) and at it's furthest it is 153 million kilometres away (in July). The Earth orbits the Sun once a year and, although we use this for our calendar, it does not make the seasons. The Earth is spinning on it's axis like a spinning top and makes one complete spin every day, giving us light in the day when we are facing the Sun and dark in the night when we are facing away from the Sun. In the past something big probably hit the Earth and tilted the axis that it spins around by 23.5 degrees. It is this tilt that gives us the seasons. In June the northern-half of the Earth is slightly closer to the Sun making it warmer (summer) and the southern-half is further away making it colder (winter). When the Earth has moved to the other side of the Sun in December the northern-half is now further away (winter) and the southern side is closer (summer). There is also a wobble to the Earth's spinning, like the wobble of a spinning top, called precession. One spin of Earth's precession takes about 26,000 years.

Earth also has a moon that is 384,400 kilometres away (about 30 Earth's diameters away). This may have formed at the same time as the large object that hit the Earth and tilted it, knocking off large lumps of rock that later came together to form the moon. The moon is relatively large, about 27% the size of the Earth, but is only 1% of Earth's mass making gravity six times less than that on Earth. The moon orbits the Earth every 27.3 days and it's phases repeat every 29.5 days. We use it's orbit to divide our year into months, and it produces the tides in the seas as the gravity of the moon pulls the water. It spins in synchronisation with the Earth so that the same half of the moon is always pointing to the Earth (called tidal locking). This does not mean that the moon has a dark side because there are times throughout it's orbit that the Sun shines on both sides of the moon, it is just that we will never see the far side from Earth. The phases of the moon are produced by the sunlight reflecting off different regions as it orbits Earth.

The Earth formed at the same time as the Sun, about 4.5 billion years ago, along with the other seven planets: Mercury, Venus, Mars, Jupiter, Saturn, Uranus and Neptune. Earth is the third planet from the Sun. There is debate about the existence of a ninth planet, called Planet 9, but we need to see it before we can confirm it exists. Pluto used to be called a planet but it is now considered to be a dwarf planet (it's smaller than the moon) and it lives within what is called the Kuiper Belt, a ring of small, icy rocks and objects orbiting the Sun beyond the most distant planet Neptune. Pluto does have a lovely heart-shaped glacier on it that was seen by the *New Horizons* inter-planetary space probe in 2015.

The Earth exists at an important distance from the Sun called the habitable zone. This is where the temperature of Earth is such that water can be a liquid, an essential requirement for life. It is also called the Goldilocks zone because it is not too hot, and not too cold, but it is just right for liquid water and life.

Planet Earth is likely to exist as long as the Sun does, which is about another 7 billion years, and in theory life could stay on the planet for 600 million years possibly. Although, how long Earth will maintain life is going to depend on us humans and how we treat it.

It was only quite recently, in 1995 [2], that we first detected a planet that orbits a star that isn't our Sun, this is called an exoplanet (an extra-solar planet). Since then over 4,000 exoplanets have been observed with the nearest one to us observed in 2016 called Proxima b [3]. This exoplanet orbits the closest star to us, Proxima Centauri, which is just over 4 light-years away.

The Sun, and all the planets, moons and objects that orbit it, form the Solar System. Almost all the matter in the Solar System is in the Sun (99.8%) and 1.3 million Earths could fit inside it. The Sun is a star that is burning hydrogen in nuclear fusion reactions. This creates the energy that is given off in heat and light that is essential for life to exist. It is a small star, in fact it is called a dwarf star (stars can get up to 150 times more massive than the Sun), but it is also a very average star, with small stars like the Sun being the most common. This is good for us because small stars live much longer than big ones.

The radiation and particles that the Sun gives out produces a solar wind. This wind is strong enough that it could blow away Earth's atmosphere if it wasn't for the magnetic field that protects it, created by it's molten iron core. This is lucky for us, not only because we need an atmosphere, but also because it stops much of the harsh radiation from the Sun that would break up molecules and stop life forming.

In 1977, two space probes were launched to explore the Solar System, *Voyager 1* and *Voyager 2*, taking flyby images of Jupiter, Saturn, Uranus and Neptune. In 2012 *Voyager 1* had travelled 14 billion kilometres (about 94 times further than the Sun is from the Earth), at a rate of 1.5 million kilometres a day, and reached the edge of the Solar System. This is the furthest any human-made object has been from Earth. *Voyager 2* left the Solar System six years later. They both continue to send data back to us as they journey outwards into interstellar space.

The Sun exists within a group of at least 250 billion other stars making up the Milky Way galaxy. The Milky Way is a small spiral galaxy with four main spiral arms . An artist's impression of the Milky Way is shown in Figure 1.3. The Sun exists on a spiral arm called the Orion Arm, at a distance of 26,000 light-years from the centre of the Milky Way, which is about a third of the way out. It would take *Voyager 1* 450 million years to reach the centre of the Milky Way at it's current speed. The Milky Way is rotating about it's centre and the Solar System with it. It takes the Sun about 230 million years to make one rotation of the Milky Way.

We think there is a black hole at the centre of the Milky Way. Although we will never see it directly, we have evidence for it from the way that stars rotate round it. In 2005, Andrea Ghez [4], plotted the orbits of some of the stars near the centre of the Milky Way and showed that they are orbiting a single point. We believe this point to be a black hole called Sagittarius A* that is four million times more massive than the Sun.

The Milky Way has been around for over 10 billion years. It has grown by swallowing up other smaller galaxies and is currently consuming the Canis

Major Dwarf Galaxy, discovered in 2003 [5], the closest galaxy to the Milky Way. It's next big collision will occur in about 4 billion years with Andromeda, a spiral galaxy similar to the Milky Way and our nearest big galaxy at about 2.5 million light-years away.

The Milky Way, Andromeda and around 30 other smaller galaxies are close enough that their gravity makes them interact with each other to form a group called the Local Group. It is about 10 million light-years across. As a galaxy group this is small, some clusters of galaxies have as many as 1,000 galaxies. The Local Group may exist within a forming supercluster of 100 galaxy groups and clusters called the Virgo Supercluster. There are estimated to be about 10 million superclusters in the universe.

At the edge of the Local Group is a vast region of relatively empty space, a void of galaxies where there are less galaxies than the average in the universe, this is called the Local Hole (or Local Void). It was discovered by Brent Tully and Rick Fisher in 1987 [6]. This hole is on a gigantic scale, possibly being as long as 1,000 million light-years and 150 million light-years wide. This may seem surprisingly big, but 90% of the universe consists of voids like this. Although some galaxies do live in voids, 90% of galaxies live in the remaining 10% of the space in the universe in a structure called the cosmic web.

So in summary, we live on a small planet, orbiting a small star, on the outer edges of a small galaxy, which is part of a small group of galaxies, that live on the edge of a massive hole in the universe. This means we are not special, although being in a place that is sparsely populated means that maybe we had less collisions with other stars and galaxies. Perhaps living in this environment made Earth a more stable place to live, giving the planet plenty of time to develop life and us to evolve as humans. Having life on Earth makes it a special place, the universe has provided a place where life can form. There may be other life out there but it is so far away that we are unlikely to ever meet it.

CHAPTER 2

The Reasoning

How do we prove that the universe evolved?
The Scientific Process: METHOD

"Science" comes from the Latin word 'scientia', meaning knowledge

2.1 WHAT IS THE SCIENTIFIC PROCESS?

How we do science

2.1.1 What is Science?

Science is a process that enables us to gain knowledge about the World and the universe that we live in. We can then use this knowledge for practical purposes to improve our lives. Science gives us a means to describe the World and provide explanations of how and why it works like it does. We gain an understanding through what we see in observations and experiments. We can also explore the World of things we cannot see directly; things from the past such as dinosaurs and unobservable things such as atoms and the centre of the Earth.

Science is generally divided into two groups of activity:

- **Natural sciences** such as Astronomy, Physics, Chemistry, Biology and Geology. These study the natural World based on observations, by looking at it and testing it, and then develop theories based on what we have observed. The natural sciences rely on being able to repeat the experiments and get the same results. These subjects are easily identified as science.

- **Social sciences** such as Psychology, Sociology, Anthropology and Economics. These are the study of human behaviours and social interactions and are also based on observations and testing. Human behaviour is un-predictable and varies between people and even for the same person on a different day. So getting repeatable observations is not as easy as with the natural sciences. In addition, doing experiments with humans has many ethical considerations and so experiments may have very small numbers of people involved, and in very limited circumstances, and this can limit the conclusions that can be reached. This means that some observations may be objective and scientific, and some may be subjec-tive and not scientific; it is necessary to be clear which work is scientific and which is not. This can be hard for scientists as well as the public to understand and can lead to misleading conclusions, especially if all the results are not published.

Then there are the activities that are not science although defining these is trickier than it may at first seem. Things that may seem scientific but are not were called 'pseudoscience' by the Austrian-British philosopher Karl Popper (1902–1994); he said they are beliefs with no evidence and are therefore not justified and are not a science. Popper classified astrology, psychoanalysis and Marxism as pseudoscience. Popper characterised pseudoscience as general, vague theories that could explain all things and made no specific falsifiable predictions. In contrast, he characterised science as providing specific, novel, risky predictions and required scientists to be willing to reject a theory if the predictions were not observed. Determining what is a science and what is not is called the 'demarcation problem'. This is not a simple problem and continues to be an active area of philosophical debate today.

So what makes a science different than a non-scientific subject? A science is a way to find out knowledge. This in itself isn't helpful unless we define knowledge. A generally accepted definition by philosophers is that knowledge is something that is true that we believe in – **knowledge is justified belief**. Scientific knowledge is justified because it comes from evidence. To help us define what is not a science we can define what is not knowledge. Something is not knowledge if:

1. We believe it but it isn't true – then it is not a science. For example, I believe my friend is Italian when in fact they are Greek.

2. It is true but we don't believe it – then we don't know it. For example, If I don't believe the Earth is a sphere.

3. It is true and we believe it but we can't know that it's true. Predicting something that happens randomly is not knowledge, for example, if I believe my friend will win the lottery and then they do, this is not knowledge because I could not have known that they were going to win on that day. This is a subtler way of identifying a pseudoscience.

So knowledge is something we believe and is true, and science is a way of gaining this knowledge by finding out about the World from evidence we have gained using observations. A simpler way of saying this is that science is evidence-based knowledge. From the evidence we gain we can reach conclusions which gives us knowledge of what is true rather than belief or opinion. What science gives us is a method to gain knowledge that is justified by the evidence.

2.1.2   The Basic Scientific Process

Scientists arrive at beliefs by a process of reasoning

THE BASIC SCIENTIFIC PROCESS

1. Gather evidence through observations and experiments

2. Make conclusions based on the evidence

3. Develop a theory to explain the evidence

4. Make predictions based on the theory

5. Gather more evidence to prove the predictions

6. Re-evaluate the conclusions and theory

Methodology is at the heart of science. How science is done is important and the methods that we use today have been developed over centuries. The basic scientific process was developed during the Scientific Revolution in the 16th and 17th centuries through the work of Copernicus, Galileo, Kepler and Newton. These scientists naturally developed and used the scientific process but it was written down and pulled together into a methodology by the English philosopher Francis Bacon (1561–1626) in his book 'Novum Organum' (translated as 'New tool') in 1620 and today it is still considered to be the core of the scientific process.

Bacon's scientific method revolves around two key concepts:

1. Observations: that are recorded without prejudice

2. Induction: making conclusions from the observations

Why was this so radical? It seems normal to us today but at that time it was thought that science was about recovering the knowledge of the Ancients particularly from the teachings of Aristotle. The Aristotelian way of gaining knowledge was by using logic and intuition, evidence and experiment was not important. This way of studying continued for over 1,500 years (through the medieval dark ages). The mindset changed due to the successes of Copernicus,

Galileo, Newton and Kepler. It took time for the new process of science to be recognised as a powerful way of gaining knowledge and to become established.

Although we think that new scientific ideas should be accepted by the strength of the evidence, in reality, like anything new, it needs to be marketed in order to get other scientists to agree and to get funding. History has shown that the scientists themselves need supporters; cheer-leaders that support what they are doing and the way they are doing it. This is especially so when a new theory or method is being proposed because scientists have to be persuaded to reject the established way of thinking and this is not easy. The need for marketing and cheer-leaders is as true today as it was 400 years ago.

This was the role of Francis Bacon, he was a cheer-leader for a new way of doing science. Bacon was part of the court of Queen Elizabeth 1 and was Lord Chancellor for two years so he had the ear of the rich and powerful and was well placed to influence the accepted view of scientific reasoning. Surprisingly, Bacon was not a supporter of the scientific ideas that were being proposed by Copernicus and Galileo (he did not believe in the heliocentric universe) but he was looking for a different way of thinking than the Aristotelian approach. Unlike his contemporaries, he believed that the Ancients didn't know everything and that there were new things to know. What made Bacon a true visionary was that he also believed that new knowledge should be used for practical purposes. He is reputed to have said "knowledge is power".

Although Bacon was part of the elite, his views on science were egalitarian. In his book he proposed that science should not be done by just a few people but by many people working together as scientists to understand the World. Today, this is how science is done. It is only through the research of numerous different types of people from around the World, working in teams, covering many different disciplines, and sharing what they learn, that we have the knowledge we have today being used to create the technological society we live in. Bacon argued for co-operation and methodology in science rather than individualism and intuition. It is these values that has made science an important and powerful tool and enabled huge changes in society.

The evidence-based methodology of science proposed by Bacon has been a powerful driver in gaining new knowledge and developing new practical applications that have changed society. This has led to some believing that this is the only way to do science. British philosopher Bertrand Russell (1872–1970) supported the belief that science is the only way to attain knowledge, a view that is called naturalism. Some take it to the next level of complete worship of the scientific process, called scientism. The opposing view believes that science is not the only way of understanding the World, that the arts, humanities and philosophy produce knowledge too. Whatever you believe, there is no doubt that the scientific process has influenced human society beyond what anyone could have imagined 400 years ago.

2.1.3 How Do We Collect Evidence?

Evidence is the foundation of scientific endeavour. Through the production and analysis of evidence, that is objective and repeatable, science becomes a powerful tool to understand the World. Evidence comes from observations of nature: looking at rocks, plants, animals, humans and stars. Evidence also comes from carrying out experiments which allows us to get evidence for the unobservable things such as radioactivity, electricity and forces. Evidence about the unobservable has to be particularly convincing for sceptics to believe it. To be convincing we have to have a clear method that is accepted by other scientists as a process that will lead to objective data. So how we collect evidence is important. Being impartial and accurate when collecting evidence is essential for good science.

How do we choose what evidence we collect? Firstly, we do what we can do at that time. This may sound obvious but it is important to recognise that we are limited by what technology is available, what ideas we have and what it is possible to do. We may be able to make predictions and think of experiments but if the right conditions, technology and ideas are not available then we cannot do the experiment so we have to wait until we can. An example of this are gravitational waves that were predicted by Albert Einstein in 1915 when he developed his general theory of relativity. It was 100 years later, in 2016, that technology had improved enough for the first gravitational waves to be detected. Sometimes we may never get the evidence we want so we have to explore alternative ways that may give us clues in a more indirect way. For example, we are unlikely to ever be able to get direct evidence that will tell us what the Big Bang was but we can develop theories that give us other clues that we may be able to test to give us indirect evidence.

Experiments are not simply gathering data but involve designing tests for our theories. Francis Bacon said that we need "to torture nature for her secrets", by which he meant that we need to do experiments in order to see what the limits of nature are. We choose from experience what to vary in experiments and we also simplify the experiments to make them understandable and reproducible. We do this by using ideal systems such as in a vacuum or using a sphere to simplify the shape. Experiments are important for a variety of reasons:

- Experiments test theories in ways that wouldn't happen otherwise, they ask 'what if?'

- Experiments need to be repeatable so that others can check the results and confirm the theory.

- Experiments need to measure things to standard agreed definitions in order to limit the subjective affects of bias and perceptions of the observer on the results.

It is common in experiments to require using random samples to reduce any subjectivity that scientists may bring to the test. 'Randomised control trials' (RCT) are used regularly in biomedical science. A control sample is one where the treatment is not performed. The outcome of the control group is then compared to the group that had the treatment to see if they had significantly better outcomes. An RCT is one where the allocation of people into the control group or the treatment group is chosen randomly and in some cases may not be known by the scientists performing the experiment (this is then called a blind experiment). Randomising the test helps to eliminate factors that are not being tested, for example, age, diet and exercise.

When there are two ideas to explain the same evidence Bacon proposed that an experiment be designed that results in a different outcome for the two ideas. This experiment will then show which idea is supported. This is called a 'perjorative instance'. However in designing the experiment we already have preconceived ideas so it could be argued that this experiment is influenced by our prejudices, something we do not want for good science. Bacon argued that this experiment should only be designed after the initial investigation has been done so that the subjectivity is acceptable.

A more recent way of collecting evidence is by using a computer. We put into a computer the rules of physics, chemistry, biology and then try out different models and see which one fits the observations. We can model the evolution of the universe by programming the laws of physics into a computer and letting it calculate the way matter evolves to create stars and galaxies. By comparing the picture of galaxies that the computer produces, to what we observe when we look at galaxies, we can see which model fits the best.

Today, there is so much knowledge in science that one person cannot know it all. It takes many years to become an expert in one particular discipline so it is necessary that, for an individual, evidence also comes from what we learn from others: from books, publications, lectures, discussions and the internet. This is not new evidence (although it is new to the individual) but it can lead to new theories and conclusions. Whether we trust this as knowledge depends on the source and how reliable we think that source is. One way of ensuring that the source is giving us 'justified knowledge' is to check that published research is of a scientific standard. This is done by requiring research to be reviewed by other scientists in a process called 'peer review'. The purpose of peer review is to check that:

- the work has used scientific methods,

- the evidence gained is without prejudice,

- the conclusions reached are justified by the evidence.

Peer review is considered an essential part of the scientific process today.

More recently there are developments that question whether we need evidence to make an idea scientific. Traditionally, it has been assumed that science is working towards understanding the reality of how the World works.

Now, it is being debated whether we can ever really know what reality is or whether we need to know reality if our non-reality theories are able to make very accurate predictions. Two theories that are driving this debate are quantum theory and string theory. Quantum theory tells us how the microscopic world of fundamental particles behaves. The theory fits the evidence very well, makes predictions to high degrees of accuracy and we use it to build complex products such as computers. Although the theory works well we cannot explain why it works. We do not know what is happening in reality but we accept it as a theory. String theory is a mathematical theory that aims to explain how the quantum world and the large-scale world fit together. There is no evidence for the theory but it is very elegant and it can be argued that if it is consistent within itself then maybe that should be sufficient to say that it is a good theory. The problem with this argument is that if we reject evidence as the basis of science then we risk rejecting the very method that has given science it's power. I like to think that we can know what reality is and I am motivated by finding out how the real World works.

2.2   CAN WE EVER REALLY PROVE SOMETHING?

Proof vs Probability

2.2.1   Scientific Reasoning, Proof and Falsification

Francis Bacon said that induction is an essential part of scientific reasoning. So what is induction? Induction is a way of reaching valid conclusions from the evidence. What do we mean by valid conclusions? It means that the conclusions need to logically flow from the evidence. This may seem obvious but poor science can result from invalid conclusions rather than bad evidence. In order to make sure that our conclusions are logical we need to understand how the arguments are made that lead us to the conclusion. So let's look at how arguments are made. An example of an argument is:

All birds can fly
Geese are birds
_____

All geese can fly

An argument has two parts:

1. **Premise** – A premise is based on the observations we have made. There can be many premises. In the example above the premises are 'All birds can fly' and 'Geese are birds'.

2. **Conclusion** – What we can truthfully and logically conclude given that the premises are true. In the example above the conclusion is that 'All geese can fly'.

The conclusions can be false even if the premises are trues and conclusions will be false if any of the premises are false. This is an area of science that can be misunderstood and misleading. So how do we make true conclusions from our evidence? There are two types of conclusions:

1. **Deduction** – The conclusion is true given that the premises are true. This can be considered as a 'proof'. The truth of the premises guarantee the truth of the conclusion.

2. **Induction** – The conclusion is a generalisation based on a sample of possible objects. In our example above, the evidence we have for the premise 'all birds can fly' must be from a sample of all birds. We have not observed all the birds in the World, only a subset of them. Therefore, the conclusion we make is inductive.

An inductive conclusion is not a proof since it contains an assumption that all the objects are the same as the observed sample, it is a conclusion from the known to the unknown. Induction is a generalisation from the specific and assumes that the laws of nature don't vary between the two. Most of science uses inductive conclusions.

Induction does not give us certainty but gives us sufficient probability not far short of certainty. In science you may think that we would only accept a deductive proof to give us certainty. Sometimes we are able to have that certainty but most of the time we cannot definitively prove something because we have to make assumptions. Scientists are often misreported as 'proving' something when in fact it has been inducted using a generalisation from the examined to the unexamined. This does not mean that the science is wrong or that the work is not scientific. It means that 'proof' is very hard to come by and we live with an element of uncertainty while seeking evidence to give us the best knowledge we can have at that time. It is an approach that has been successfully used over the past 400 years.

The use of induction in science was questioned by the philosopher David Hume (1711–1776) in his book "*An Enquiry Into Human Understanding*". Hume said that, although we use induction all the time in life, it is a "brute animal" and cannot be rationally justified so we should not use it. This is 'Hume's problem of induction'. It says that the process of induction, which is a key element of the scientific process, does not give us justified knowledge therefore it cannot be part of the scientific process. Hume's argument is a blow to the scientific process as laid out by Francis Bacon. This philosophical problem is still debated today.

Hume's problem of induction provoked Karl Popper to explore how science could only use deduction. He wrote his findings in his book "*The Logic of Scientific Discovery*" (1934). He believed that Hume had shown the 'unjustifiability of induction' and therefore science should not rely upon it. Popper developed the concept of 'falsification' and argued that although we may never prove a theory is true by sampling a small quantity, it is possible to prove a

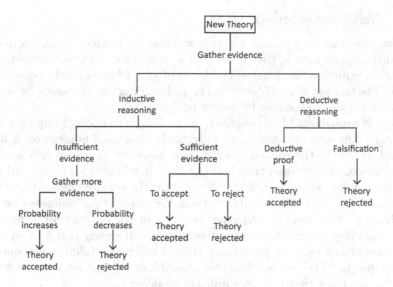

Figure 2.1: Flowchart showing the deductive and inductive processes for accepting or rejecting a theory. Credit: C. Devereux and P. Farrell.

theory false by just one example of it not being true. For example, the premise 'All geese are white' is proved false by observing one grey goose. The conclusion becomes 'It is false that all geese are white': a deductive proof. The logic of Popper's argument means that scientists should be working to show that their theories are false rather than that they are true. This is not how people work though. The focus of scientist's research is, generally, to prove that their ideas are right. Despite this shortcoming, the concept of falsification still has a role in science; a theory can be disproved using falsification and experiments should be devised to test theories based on falsification. Publishing a theory allows others to see if there are ways to falsify it.

Popper's theory of falsification did not change the need for induction in science but it did lead him to set out criteria to distinguish between science and pseudoscience by identifying 'good' science as:

- A critical attitude to the received wisdom.

- An insistence on evidence-based content that is precise and wide in scope.

- The use of creative thinking to solve problems with bold conjectures that open up radical new possibilities for experiment and observations.

- The ideas of ad-hocness, novel prediction and scientific corroboration.

2.2.2 Probability as Science

By now, you may be sceptical about how robust scientific knowledge really is. Inductive reasoning is the basis of most scientific work but cannot give certainty. Deductive reasoning is the basis of proof but is rarely possible in science. The concept of probability can help. Even if a theory cannot be shown to be true it can be shown to be highly probable.

What is probability? It is how likely something is to occur. Flipping a coin is a random process and has an equally likely chance of landing on a head or a tail. If we flip the coin once we do not know which way it will land. If we flip the coin many times then half the time it will land on heads and half the time it will land on tails. The more we flip the coin the closer the result will be to exactly 50% heads and 50% tails. We can now put a number on the probability and we have an objective measure of the outcome of a flip of a coin. Probability can also be a subjective measure. If we say that finding alien life on Mars has a very low probability then it will mean different amounts to different people. There is no objective probability, we cannot put a number on it, we just know that it is very unlikely to occur.

Thomas Bayes was a 17th century English clergyman who pioneered probability theory and discovered the principle of conditionality; the probability of something occurring is based on whether it has occurred before. As more evidence supports a theory, there is more confidence in that theory and a scientist's rational belief in the theory should change. A difficulty with this approach is knowing what probability to put on the theory before the evidence is collected, often this is a subjective best guess. This subjective element can be unwelcome by some scientists but it does not stop Bayes' approach being widely used particularly in analysing the statistics of experiments and is an important part of the scientific method for many disciplines.

Using probability within scientific reasoning provides an adaptation to the scientific method:

1. have an initial probability that the theory is true,

2. get evidence to support or refute the theory,

3. update the probability in light of new evidence by following the principle of conditionality.

2.3 HOW TO MAKE THEORIES AND REVOLUTIONS

Changing scientific ideas

2.3.1 How Do We Make Theories?

A scientific theory is an explanation that has been shown to fit the evidence, it answers the why question. Why does the World behave as we are observing it? In science, a theory and a model mean different things. The following are definitions of types of scientific explanations.

- **A Scientific Fact** is a statement supported by evidence. An example is 'everyday the sun rises in the East and sets in the West'. Facts can change as observations and measurement techniques improve.

- **A Scientific Law** is a description of the relationship between things that is supported by lots of evidence from different sources. Laws are often mathematical statements. Newton's Law of Gravity is a law because it provides a description of how the Earth orbits the Sun but not why. Laws do not explain the causes and can have exceptions.

- **A Scientific Theory** is an in-depth explanation of why something behaves as it does that has been extensively tested. It gives the causes for the laws based on evidence. Einstein's theory of relativity is a theory because it determines the causes of gravity as the distortion of spacetime. A theory can be tested to determine how accurate it is. If there is more than one theory to explain a piece of evidence it is said to be 'under-determined'. In this case we cannot determine the true causes of the evidence we are observing and we need more evidence.

- **A Scientific Principle** is a rule by which a phenomena works. A principle is more specific than a law and may be more restricted when it can be used. An example is the cosmological principle which describes the uniformity of the universe. There is no mathematical equation for this, it is a description of a concept that is supported by evidence.

- **A Scientific Hypothesis** is a statement, such as, if A happens then B will happen, that has not yet been shown to be true. Scientists work on hypotheses derived from theories, laws and evidence in order to extend knowledge. An example of an hypothesis is that small variations in the orbits of the outer planets of the Solar System could mean that an unseen planet exists that has yet to be found called Planet 9. An hypothesis needs to be testable.

- **A Scientific Model** is a tool to help aid scientific thinking about how the World works. There are different purposes to developing a model:

  – To simplify the World or phenomenon so we can understand it.

  – A starter model that can be built on to develop the full theory.

  – A specific case of a phenomenon.

  – To represent reality until a theory is established.

  – A computer simulation using the laws to provide tests of theories.

Models are used in the daily work of a scientist. In cosmology, ΛCDM is a model that is being built on to develop a full theory.

Now we know what a scientific theory is, the next step is to know how to develop a theory and, of course, there are theories on how to develop theories. Here are four important ideas about how to make scientific explanations.

1. **Hempel's Covering Law**. The German philosopher Carl Hempel (1905–1997) said a scientific explanation must include reference to a scientific law and some initial conditions or particular facts. This is called the Covering Law because the thing to be explained is 'covered' by at least one general law of nature. Hempel asserted that an explanation is potentially a prediction and a prediction based on evidence is potentially an explanation.

2. **Harman's Inference to Best Explanation** (IBE). American philosopher Gilbert Harman (1938-) proposed that theories are chosen by picking the best explanation to fit as much of the evidence as possible. Although this may seem obvious it has been an influential method use widely by scientists.

3. **Occam's Razor** (also called the Law of Parsimony). William of Occam (1285–1349) was an English philosopher and monk who stated the principle *"pluralitas non est ponenda sine necessitate"* (plurality should not be posited without necessity). It is interpreted as 'do not make things more complicated than necessary'. If there are two theories, then the simplest explanation is the one to pick. This rule is widely quoted and used. We have to be careful with this approach though; the universe is a complicated place and the simplest answer may not be the right one.

4. **Kuhn's Ideas on Scientific Theory**. Thomas Kuhn (1922–1996) was an American philosopher who developed radical ideas about scientific revolutions and how scientists develop theories. Kuhn said that a scientific theory should:

   (a) Be based on accurate observations.

   (b) Fit with other accepted theories in the subject.

   (c) Be able to explain more than just what it was designed for.

   (d) Be as simple as possible (Occam's Razor).

   (e) Be able to lead to other research.

2.3.2 Revolutionary Science

Cosmology in crisis

Science seeks to get the same result when an experiment or observation is repeated, regardless of who is doing the experiment and what their beliefs are. This is what is meant by science being objective, it is a fundamental principle

of the basic scientific process proposed by Francis Bacon. However, the ability
for science to be truly objective has been questioned over the centuries.

The basic scientific process, of drawing rational conclusions from observations in an objective way, comes under the category of 'naive inductivism'.
Why is it called naive? In reality doing science is more complicated than being
purely rational. Scientists are people and, no matter how hard we try, we will
bring our beliefs, assumptions and unconscious biases into our work. Scientists live and work within a society and culture that also brings it's own set
of beliefs and prejudices and this will have an impact on the work too. The
view that science can be subjective as well as objective is called 'sophisticated
inductivism' – we reach conclusions in a more sophisticated way than by using
pure logic and, in this context, sophisticated means subjective or non-rational.

So how can being subjective and non-rational still be considered as being
scientific? It can if it is applied to the discovery of new ideas. Consider how
someone comes up with a new idea or a new type of experiment; it is a creative
process. How people come up with creative ideas is not really understood but
we know that it need not be rational; it can come from a dream, a belief,
from religion, from thinking random thoughts, from watching TV or talking
to someone about something totally unconnected. Creativity is a subjective
process; and yet it is an important part of doing science. How can we reconcile
these two processes, the rational justified knowledge and the non-rational
creative ideas for new discoveries?

In the first half of the 20th century there were three main approaches to
this reconciliation.

1. David Hume's problem of induction showed that reaching conclusions
   using induction is logically irrational but that it is the best way we have
   of doing science. Even today, the problem has not been resolved but we
   continue using induction anyway because it works. Hume's approach to
   science was that it is inductive but non-rational.

2. Karl Popper considered that non-rational science had an importance in
   the process of inspiration and discovery but he maintained, particularly
   through his arguments of falsification, that knowledge requires ratio-
   nality. Popper's approach to science was that it is non-inductive and
   rational.

3. The German philosopher Rudolph Carnap was a leading exponent of the
   view that rejected non-rationality in science completely (called logical
   empiricism). He believed that science can be fully rational if we solve
   the details of precise logic (often using the mathematics of statistics and
   probability). Carnap's approach is an inductive and rational approach
   to science.

In the 1960s, a new scientific reasoning was introduced into the debate and
revolutionised the way we view the scientific process. Thomas Kuhn (1922–
1996) was a philosopher and also a physicist and historian. Rather than rely

on existing versions of how scientific ideas were changed, Kuhn studied the
key scientific revolutions from the perspective of an historian. He started with
the Copernican revolution and realised that the acceptance of the heliocentric
universe was not simply about scientific evidence and reasoning winning the
argument over religious dogma. What actually happened was far more complicated. He studied other revolutions in science and wrote his findings in "*The
Structure of Scientific Revolutions*". This has been an influential book in the
management of science and the way we think about scientific methodology
today. It brought about an acceptance that science is, and can be, done in a
non-rational way and still be science.

Kuhn argued that each scientific discipline has it's own set of preferred
skills, methods and theories that provides the framework of that discipline.
He called this the 'paradigm' that scientists work in. It includes the successful
parts of the science that an individual learns that provides them with the basis
for all their future scientific work, for example, all the standard problems and
solutions that are practised at school. The word 'paradigm' is now widely used
due to Kuhn, and can be considered as 'the way we look at the World or a
situation'.

Kuhn divided the scientific process into two activities:

- **Normal science**. The day-to-day activity of a scientist, working within
  the current paradigm, to gather new evidence in order to confirm the
  accepted theories and solve minor problems within those theories. Kuhn
  called this 'puzzle-solving' where the strict rules for solving the problems
  are determined by the paradigm. Kuhn said "Normal science does and
  must continually strive to bring theory and fact into closer agreement,
  and that activity can easily be seen as testing or as a search for confirmation or falsification". He went on to say that "Failure to achieve a
  solution discredits only the scientist and not the theory".

- **Science in crisis**. This is when an existing paradigm is changed and
  revolutions can happen. A science is in crisis when an increasing number
  of problems occur in the current paradigm, Kuhn called these 'anomalies'. As the number of anomalies increase, then more scientists will work
  on the anomalies until the paradigm is seen as being in crisis. Crises are
  most likely to happen when anomalies question the most fundamental
  principles of a paradigm, or stand in the way of an application, or cause
  the paradigm to be criticised.

Kuhn's study of scientific revolutions turned up some unexpected results
that challenged the accepted views at the time. Previously it was assumed
that science was a cumulative growth of knowledge, a view encapsulated in the
famous quote by Newton "If I have seen further than others it is by standing
upon the shoulders of giants". Kuhn said this is not how revolutions happen.
They are not achieved in a gradual way but are a comprehensive change
of the view of the World – a 'paradigm shift' – and result in a new way of

practising science and a new set of problems to investigate. Revolutions require an abandonment of past theories but, importantly, the abandoned theories do not become unscientific since they were also developed from similar scientific reasoning and methods that we use today.

Kuhn also said that revolutions only happen when a viable alternative view is available as well as scientists to support the new view who can persuade other scientists of it's validity. He said "Most scientists most of the time are committed to their paradigm and work to prove it even in the face of refuting evidence".

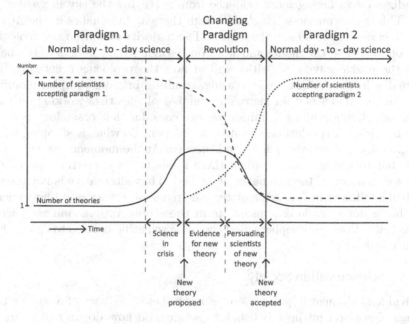

Figure 2.2: Revolutions in science. When science is in crisis the number of theories goes up and the number of scientists supporting the paradigm goes down. A change in theory does not happen quickly but takes time for scientists to accept the new paradigm. Credit: C. Devereux and P. Farrell.

Kuhn's exploration of revolutions in science showed that evidence alone is not enough to get a paradigm shift. When one serious anomaly occurs then it is often not questioned by the scientific community. When more occur then some scientists begin to question the core assumptions that the paradigm is based on, for example, is the universe expanding? Alternatives are often proposed by younger scientists or mavericks who are not invested in the previous paradigm, their career does not depend on the success of the old paradigm, instead, their career could be made by the success of a new paradigm. Which scientists are part of a revolution will depend on their psychology – are they a risk taker, a lone voice, which social groups are they in, where do they work etc.?

It is not easy to challenge the accepted scientific views and new paradigms take time to establish. Often in the beginning, new paradigms do not explain all the evidence that the existing paradigm does, and it takes time to establish that the new paradigm fits with the evidence and solves some of the anomalies. A new paradigm also creates new problems that will become the new puzzle-solving of normal science.

How does this relate to cosmology? The normal day-to-day activity of cosmologists is working within the ΛCDM model of the evolving universe, this is the current paradigm. The aim of our work is to extend the success of this paradigm by gathering more evidence from surveying the sky in greater detail. This is the 'puzzle-solving'. Although there are anomalies in the ΛCDM model, cosmologists do not abandon it. The majority of working cosmologists are committed to the model and work on resolving the conflicts in the belief that the puzzle-solving activities will answer the problems eventually. The anomalies in the ΛCDM are increasing, resulting in more complex modifications to the model and an increasing number of scientists working on these anomalies. Using Kuhn's definition we can consider that cosmology is a 'science in crisis'. A revolution is waiting to happen. So what is stopping it? As Kuhn said, an alternative paradigm is needed. At the moment, we have many ideas but to change the paradigm there needs to be one strong alternative that solves many of the anomalies of ΛCDM. That alternative is not there.

Kuhn followed in Bacon's footsteps; he made observations on how science was being done, made conclusions from those observations and then wrote them down. Both philosophers used the basic scientific process to change how science is done.

2.3.3 Science within Society

As Kuhn so eloquently pointed out, scientists exist as part of a society that brings biases and intrinsic beliefs into science. So how do we make sure we are being scientific and that the work is being done in an objective way? Scientists work within the ethical framework of being honest in our work to ensure that it is carried out objectively, that the data is interpreted correctly and that the conclusions drawn are relevant and justified. This is policed by publishing the work so that others can test the science, repeat observations and validate conclusions. There is the added check of peer review. Before publishing a paper, or agreeing funding for a project, the work is reviewed by another scientist in the discipline who can confirm that the work has been done scientifically. We have scientific committees and funding bodies that apply ethics to what is funded and to how the research is done. These bodies have an essential role in science and society.

The scientific process is important, our society is based on the results of it so everyone has a part to play in it. Scientific education is key, not just about the knowledge but also the process itself. It helps the public to not be misled by false science, it helps society decide which science is funded and it helps science to be used in ways that enhances life for everyone.

CHAPTER 3

The Clues

What are the clues that tell us how the universe behaves?
The Scientific Process: RESULTS

'Cosmological Clues' is the evidence we have gathered

3.1   WHAT IS A COSMOLOGICAL CLUE?

Evidence for the Standard Model of Cosmology

We have seen in the previous chapter that getting evidence through observations and experiments is an important part of the scientific process. We gather the clues and then make theories based on the clues, much like detective work. In cosmology, our clues are based on what we see when we look up at the sky. To be a scientific clue it should be independent of any theory or model and as scientists we state the laws and assumptions that our observations are based on. A Cosmological Clue is a scientific fact, a statement supported by evidence, and it gives us evidence about how the universe behaves. Any theory or model must explain these pieces of evidence.

The six Cosmological Clues that are discussed in this chapter are observations that are the key findings leading to the Standard Model of Cosmology that we have today. Each clue adds to the picture we have of how the universe formed and evolved, and each clue has been confirmed by many scientists and from different experiments so are accepted as reliable observations.

The first clue came in 1929 when Edwin Hubble observed that most galaxies were moving away from us (Clue 1). This led to the theory that the universe is expanding. If we extrapolate backwards in time the universe must have started from an extremely small state, called the Big Bang. It is Hubble's clue that can be considered as the start of the subject of cosmology – the study of how the universe evolved.

Then there are the clues for dark matter. The main clue comes from observations of how galaxies rotate (Clue 2); they rotate in a way that means there needs to be much more matter in them than we can see in the stars. Fritz Zwicky was the first to observe this in 1933 when looking at galaxy clusters. He proposed that there is significant unseen matter in the universe but this was ignored by the scientific community, being seen as too radical an idea. It was not until 1970, when Vera Rubin saw the same phenomena when looking at rotations of galaxies, that the existence of dark matter became accepted as a possibility. James Peebles received a Nobel prize in 2019 for his theoretical work on galaxy rotations along with much more that he contributed to cosmology. The clue that allowed dark matter to be accepted by the scientific community came from observations of the large-scale structure of the universe (Clue 5). In 1987, surveys of large numbers of galaxies revealed that galaxies are not randomly spread out throughout the sky but they follow a pattern that looks like a three-dimensional spider's web, called the cosmic web. The explanation of how this forms requires the addition of dark matter into our model.

The next clue became the piece of evidence that confirmed the Big Bang must have happened and led to it's general acceptance – the discovery of the Cosmic Microwave Background (CMB) in 1964 by Penzias and Wilson (Clue 3). This discovery was so significant that they received the Nobel prize for their work in 1978. A further Nobel prize was awarded for work on the CMB to George Smoot and John Mather in 2006. Of all the clues, this is the hardest to explain if the Big Bang did not happen. A further confirmation clue came in the 1980s from measurements of hydrogen and helium in the universe (Clue 4). The ratio of hydrogen to helium cannot be explained by stars alone but can be explained by the nuclear processes that would have occurred in the first few minutes after the Big Bang. The work that calculated the nuclear processes in stars that was necessary to understand this clue received a Nobel prize, awarded to William Fowler in 1983.

The final clue discussed in this section is the discovery of dark energy (Clue 6). In 1998, Adam Riess, Brian Schmidt and Saul Perlmutter observed that supernovae, which are explosions of dying stars, are moving away from us faster than predicted by Hubble expansion, in fact they are moving away at an accelerating rate. For an object to accelerate a force is required, even stars in deep space. We don't know what this force is, but it must have an energy and we can see the effect it is having on the stars, so we call it dark energy. The evidence is so compelling that dark energy is included in the Standard Model of Cosmology and the scientists received the Nobel prize for their work in 2011. Five Nobel prizes for six Cosmological Clues tells us how important these observations have been to the scientific community.

3.2 CLUE 1: THE EXPANDING UNIVERSE

The Hubble-Lemaître Law

The story of the expanding universe starts with American astronomer Vesto Slipher working at the Lowell Observatory in Arizona. In 1912, Slipher was taking measurements of the Andromeda galaxy, a spiral galaxy similar to the Milky Way and is the nearest big galaxy to us (astronomers call it M31). By looking at the spectrum of the light coming from Andromeda, Slipher could tell whether the galaxy was moving towards us or away from us. He used a technique called the Doppler shift. We can hear this when an ambulance drives past us with it's siren blasting. As the ambulance moves towards us the sound waves are closer together and the siren sound has a higher pitch than when it drives away from us when the pitch gets lower as the sound waves become further apart. Figure 3.1 shows the principle of Doppler shift. (Next time a siren passes you listen to the change in sound.) Light waves behave in the same way and we can see the spectrum of light being squashed if the star is moving towards us or expanded if it is moving away from us. Today, this technique is used extensively in astronomy and we call it the measurement of galactic redshift.

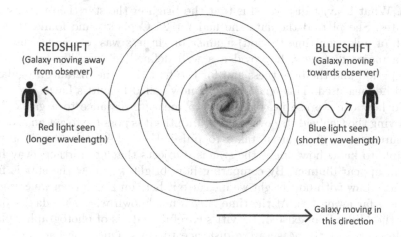

Figure 3.1: The Doppler Shift. When a galaxy moves towards an observer light is compressed and becomes bluer. When the galaxy is moving away the light is stretched and becomes redder. Since most galaxies are moving away from Earth this effect is called redshift in astronomy. Credit: C. Devereux and P. Farrell.

What Slipher [7] found was that the Andromeda galaxy is moving towards us at a rate of 300 kms^{-1} and we now think that it will collide with the Milky Way in about 4.5 billion years. Fortunately, this is a long way in the future and we don't have to worry about that today. The technique of measuring the speed of galaxies, and whether they are moving towards us or away from us, is the first building block to measuring the expansion of the universe. By 1925, Slipher had measured the velocity (the speed plus direction) of 40 more galaxies creating an important catalogue of data. What he found was that most of them are moving away from us. This information on it's own is interesting but to make it really interesting we would like to know the distance to each galaxy. Calculating distances in astronomy is a difficult thing to do but other astronomers were working on this.

The next building block to discovering the expanding universe was put in place by another American astronomer, Henrietta Swan Leavitt [8], who was working as a 'computer' at the Harvard College Observatory. Women were not allowed to work on the telescopes at that time so she was studying photographic plates and cataloguing the brightness of stars from the closest and smallest galaxies to us called the Small Magellanic Cloud and the Large Magellanic Cloud (they are so close to us that when you see them in the sky they look like clouds). The closeness of the galaxies allowed Leavitt to measure the brightness of individual stars. She was interested in variable stars called Cepheids which are very bright, supergiant stars that pulsate and their brightness changes with a regular period of time varying between 1 to 60 days. What Leavitt discovered is that the brighter the star then the faster it pulsates. She plotted the data she had for 25 Cepheids and found that the graph of pulsation time (period) against brightness was a straight line. This was a major discovery. It provided a well defined relationship between the time period and the brightness and for the first time the distance to galaxies could be measured. This relationship is now called Leavitt's Law.

So how can we use Leavitt's Law to measure distance to a galaxy? By observing the Cepheid star over days or months it is possible to get an accurate measurement of the time it takes to pulse. Using Leavitt's Law it is then possible to know how bright the star is. Objects that are further away from us will appear dimmer. By comparing how bright we know the star is from Leavitt's Law with how bright we measure it here on Earth then we can work out how far away it is. At the time it was not known whether galaxies other than the Milky Way existed. Leavitt's careful analysis of photographic plates developed a way to measure the distance to stars. Once she had developed the technique to measure the distance to a star then it became possible to know the distance to the galaxy that the star lives in. Since Leavitt was not allowed to make observations she could not use her work to look at galaxies, but American astronomer Edwin Hubble did, and he discovered that there were stars that existed much further away than the Milky Way. This was a fundamental discovery that showed us that other galaxies do exist and changed our view of the universe. Today, Leavitt's Law is used to measure the distance to stars and galaxies, and Cepheid stars have become what we call a 'standard

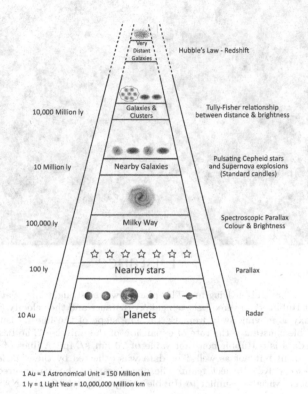

Figure 3.2: Cosmological Distance Ladder. Measuring the distance to galaxies requires the use of the distance ladder. Each rung of the ladder builds on the rung before and uses a different technique. Credit: C. Devereux and P. Farrell.

candle' – objects that we can know how far away they are. They form a key rung of the 'Cosmological Distance Ladder', shown in Figure 3.2, where each rung uses different techniques to measure the distance to objects and each rung builds on the rung before. In this way we can measure the vast distances to far off galaxies.

The final building block for this Cosmological Clue comes from work by Edwin Hubble who put the observations of Slipher and Leavitt together. Hubble was working on a new telescope that was the largest in the World at the time, the 2.5 m Hooker telescope at the Mount Wilson Observatory in California. This was powerful enough to identify individual stars in galaxies and measure their distance. Hubble had the velocity data of 46 galaxies from Slipher's measurements and he used the telescope to measure the distance to

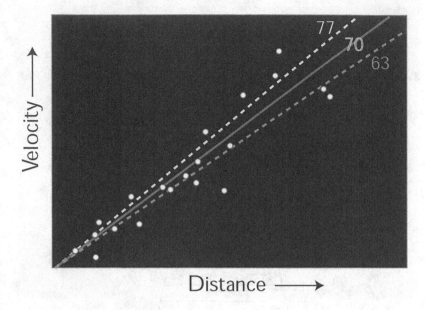

Figure 3.3: Hubble Diagram. This plot shows the straight line relationship that Hubble discovered between galaxy distance and the velocity that the galaxy is moving away from Earth. The slope of the line measures the Hubble constant – the rate of expansion of the universe. The best fit to the data is a Hubble constant value of 70 km/s/Mpc. Values of 77 and 63 can fit but not as well. The data was collected by the *Hubble Space Telescope* Key Project team. The distances have been measured using Cepheid variables similar to Hubble's original graph. Credit: NASA and ESA.

24 of these galaxies using Cepheid stars. Four of the galaxies are travelling towards us (these are all nearby galaxies) and the rest are travelling away from us. In 1929, Hubble published a paper titled "*A relation between distance and radial velocity among extra-galactic nebulae*" [9] and in it he plotted the velocity of the galaxies against their distance (shown in Figure 3.3). What he found was that the graph was a straight line; there is a simple relationship between velocity and distance, the more distant the galaxy the faster it is travelling away from us. This was an amazing discovery and changed the way we view the universe. Since then there have been many other measurements of galaxies, using different types of stars and much improved telescopes, and they show the same straight line relationship even out to much greater distances. Hubble's result has been confirmed by many different scientists and by different methods and is now accepted as a law – Hubble's Law.

The interpretation of Hubble's discovered relationship is that the universe is expanding. As the universe expands each galaxy will see all the other galaxies moving away from it and no galaxy will have a unique point in space. The more distant a galaxy is then the faster it will be moving away and the closer a galaxy is then the slower it is moving away. An analogy is dots on the surface of a balloon as it is being blown up (see Figure 3.4). Whichever dot you pick then all the other dots will get further away from it as the balloon expands. An expanding space works on the same principle but in three dimensions, it is a volume expanding rather than a surface.

Figure 3.4: The expansion of the universe showing how each galaxy is expanding away from all the other galaxies. Credit: Shutterstock.

The exceptions to Hubble's Law are the very closest galaxies to us, they may appear to be moving towards us. All galaxies, including the Milky Way, move through space relative to each other independent of the universe's expansion. If a galaxy is moving towards us faster than we see the universe expanding then the galaxy is observed as moving towards us. This only happens with the closest galaxies such as Andromeda. In Hubble's paper he did not propose an expanding universe. Hubble's interpretation was based on a static universe, which was the accepted model at that time, and he proposed that the Doppler shifts arose from the slowing down of time at large distances, what is called 'tired light'. Even in 1929 this was not accepted as a good interpretation but Hubble's observations were, and still are, accepted as good evidence. Hubble's Law is an important Cosmological Clue.

The history of science is often not neat and simple. Although Hubble is credited with discovering the expansion of the universe, there were two other scientists who published the idea of an expanding universe before Hubble's publication [10, 11]: George Lemaître in 1927 and Howard Robertson in 1928. George Lemaître was a Belgian astronomer, mathematician and priest. He

used Einstein's theory of relativity to propose that the universe exploded
from a small, "primeval super-atom" that we now call the Big-Bang. He went
further and said that this would result in galaxies moving away from us as
had been observed by Slipher earlier. Lemaître's work was theoretical, based
on the mathematics of the problem, and he did not have the evidence for
his work until Hubble's observations. Despite this, Lemaître's interpretations
became the foundation of the Standard Model of Cosmology. He was twice
nominated for a Nobel prize for this work and for his work on the structure of
atoms, although he never won it. So why was Lemaître's work not recognised
at the time? Probably because he published in French in a journal which was
not widely read. Also possibly because he lived in Belgium and his work was
not well known in America. Today, we do recognise his contribution and in
2018 members of the International Astronomical Union recommended that
Hubble's Law now be known as the Hubble-Lemaître Law.

The Hubble-Lemaître Law is summarised in one value called Hubble's
constant. This is the constant that relates galaxy velocity to distance (the
gradient of the straight line of the graph). Although it is a constant over all of
space today, it does in fact change it's value with time. Once again Lemaître
was overlooked when naming the constant since he first estimated it's value
three years before Hubble. Hubble's constant uses the symbol H_0, where H
stands for Hubble and the $_0$ means the value that it is today (astronomers
define the present time as zero, t=0). Hubble measured the value as $H_0 =
500 \text{kms}^{-1}\text{Mpc}^{-1}$. The value of H_0 is given in terms of how fast an object
is moving away from us in kilometres per second (kms^{-1}), for each unit of
distance which we measure in mega-parsecs (Mpc). A parsec is a measurement
of distance that astronomers like to use; it is 30 million million kilometres or
3.3 light-years (one light-year is the distance light travels in one year). A mega-
parsec is a million parsecs. In astronomy we are dealing with vast distances and
if we used kilometres the numbers get too big, it makes calculations simpler
if we use parsecs.

Lemaître had estimated a value of $625 \text{ kms}^{-1}\text{Mpc}^{-1}$ which was close to
Hubble's observed value of 500. Today, we get a much smaller value of about
70. Why is it so different? We now know that Hubble made an assumption
in his calculations that was incorrect. This comes from Leavitt's Law. The
constant that was used in Leavitt's Law, although correct for the data at the
time, we now know was seven times too large, so when Hubble calculated
the distance to Cepheid stars the value he got was seven times too small. If
Hubble had used the correct values of distance then his estimate of H_0 would
have given him a value of $71 \text{ kms}^{-1}\text{Mpc}^{-1}$ which is the same as we get today.

The distances that Hubble measured were wrong because he used wrong
assumptions in his calculations. It was not a mistake because at the time the
assumptions were based on the data that Hubble had. Today, we have more
data that shows that those assumptions were not correct. That is the process of
science; get data, make assumptions, get more data and test the assumptions,
and in that way we improve our measurements and our knowledge. Today,

we still have inaccuracies and we take care to identify the inaccuracies (called errors) as well as the assumptions that we use.

An important piece of information that we can get from the Hubble constant is the age of the universe. By assuming that the universe is expanding at the rate of the Hubble constant we can work out an age for the universe. The calculation is a simple one, it is 1 divided by H_0 which has the units of time. From this we calculate that the universe is 13,800 million years old (13.8 Gyr). This is the time from the Big Bang to today. The exact age depends on the model that is used for the calculation but generally the age of about 14 billion years is the working age we use. When Hubble first estimated the age from his results in 1929 it was only 2 billion years old, but radioactive dating in geology had shown that the Earth was at least 4.5 billion years. This was a big stumbling block to getting the expansion model accepted. It was only when later data produced an age of 14 billion years old that expansion was taken more seriously.

The Hubble-Lemaître Law is fundamental in astronomy. It is used as the basis of many of our calculations and observations so the more accurate our measurement of H_0 is the more accurate other measurements in cosmology are generally. We have measured H_0 using different methods and as the measurements have got more accurate we find that there is some disagreement depending on whether we are looking at the young universe or the old universe. Measurements based on observations of galaxies (the older universe) give us a value similar to Hubble between 72 and 74 $kms^{-1}Mpc^{-1}$, and measurements based on when the universe was young give us a smaller value between 67 and 68 $kms^{-1}Mpc^{-1}$. There is a discrepancy here which astronomers call the Hubble tension (this is discussed further in Section 6.5). It could be due to some physics that we don't know about yet, or it could be that our measurements need improving, or it could be telling us that our model needs to change. Needless to say this is a problem that astronomers are actively working on and it could be that the answer gives us more Cosmological Clues.

3.3   CLUE 2: THE EXISTENCE OF DARK MATTER

Anomalous rotation of galaxies

Dark matter is a strange thing. We believe it exists but we don't know what it is and we have never detected a dark matter particle. So how do we know it exists? What evidence do we have to make us think that it exists at all? The evidence for dark matter is our next Cosmological Clue.

The main evidence for dark matter comes from measuring the mass of galaxies, we weigh them (although an object in space does not have a weight so we call it 'mass'). This may seem like an impossible task but there are many ways of determining the mass of a galaxy. The first clue for dark matter came almost a century ago in 1933 from a Swiss astronomer, Fritz Zwicky, [12] when he was looking at the movement of clusters of galaxies.

Zwicky was born in Bulgaria, raised in Switzerland and worked most of his life in California. He had an extraordinary mind and contributed to many areas of science. But Zwicky was, in his own words, a 'lone wolf', the type of scientist that science needs but doesn't necessarily embrace. His abrasiveness to his colleagues made him unpopular and an outsider, but as we saw in Chapter 2, science needs outsiders especially when scientific revolutions are happening. Zwicky had an active imagination and came up with many wild ideas that were not approved of by his colleagues. Some ideas remain wild (like moving the whole Solar System to a habitable planet of another star) but some ideas have been shown to be correct and have become mainstream science; he first proposed what a neutron star is, he coined the term 'supernova', proposed that supernova were the source of cosmic rays and developed a catalogue of 120 supernovae over 50 years, he hypothesised that galaxies could deflect light and become gravitational lenses (which was confirmed 45 years later), he developed an extensive catalogue of galaxies, and, if that was not enough, he developed the underwater jet and engines for jet-assisted take-off. Despite the importance of all of this work, what he is best known for is his evidence that the universe is mostly made of dark matter.

Zwicky was making observations using the Mount Wilson telescope (the one that Hubble was using) and was looking at the rotation of the Coma Cluster. Just as a galaxy is a group of stars held together by gravity centred around a black hole, a galaxy cluster is a collection of galaxies that are held together by gravity and centre on a group of very large galaxies. The Coma Cluster is about 25 million light-years diameter, 330 million light-years away from us, and has about a thousand galaxies in it. There are two very large galaxies near the centre of the cluster that are each ten times brighter than our neighbouring galaxy Andromeda.

The galaxies within the Coma Cluster move at speeds averaging 1,000 km/s. Zwicky measured the motions of the galaxies and used gravitational equations to calculate how much matter needs to be in the cluster to keep the galaxies from flying off. He also measured how much matter there is in the cluster from the brightness of the cluster, the more stars in it the brighter it is. What Zwicky found was that the two numbers were not the same. There was not enough matter in the stars to create enough gravity to hold the galaxies in the cluster. There needed to be much, much more matter than could be seen.

Zwicky estimated that the amount of extra matter in the Coma Cluster was 400 times the amount of matter in the stars. Today, we estimate it to be about nine times. Zwicky had overestimated the amount of dark matter because the Hubble constant value that was used at that time was too large. But his general conclusion, that there is a lot of unseen matter, is valid.

Fritz Zwicky was not the first to propose that there was unseen matter. In 1922, the British physicist, James Jeans [13], proposed that there are three times more dark stars than visible stars in the Milky Way and Dutch astronomers, Jacobus Kapteyn [14] and Jan Oort [15], also found the same thing. Zwicky's work went further and showed that there was extra matter in galaxies beyond our own Milky Way and that it was a significant amount. He called this extra matter 'Dunkle Materie', translated as 'Dark Matter', a term that has stuck.

The idea that the universe is made up of mostly matter that we cannot see, know nothing about and does not fit with our understanding of particle physics was a very radical idea, one that the scientific community found difficult to accept, especially since Zwicky's personal style meant that other scientists were less inclined to listen to him. This resulted in the evidence that Zwicky presented being ignored for the next 40 years.

The acceptance of dark matter by the scientific community came during the 1970s. Astronomers were getting anomalous measurements of the mass of nearby galaxies and were debating about whether this was due to unseen movements within the galaxies distorting the way the stars move or whether it was due to dark matter. In 1970, Vera Rubin [16], an American Astronomer and pioneer of advancing women into science, published a paper on the rotation of the Andromeda galaxy which seemed to show that there was more mass in it than we could see. In the same year, Ken Freeman saw the same effect when using radio waves. In 1973, Morton Roberts and Arnold Rots did the same measurements on more galaxies and found the same result. In 1974, Jerry Ostriker and James Peebles [17] in America, and separately Jaan Einasto [18] in the Soviet Union, refined the model for calculating how galaxies rotate. They also measured the way interacting galaxies move and determined that there was ten times more unseen matter. Peebles even went on to predict how much of this unseen mass is in the total universe. This was still not sufficient evidence to convince the general scientific community. The rotation measurements were not accurate enough to be conclusive and maybe the galaxies weren't interacting. In 1975, two conferences were held where the case for dark matter was hotly debated. Was there missing matter and if so is it gas we can't see or very faint, unseen stars? No conclusion was reached. More clues were needed.

The clinching clues were provided in 1978. Vera Rubin [19] published the rotation data of ten galaxies using visible light and Albert Bosma [20] published his PhD thesis that had the rotation data of 25 galaxies using radio waves. It was Rubin's data that is recognised as providing enough evidence for dark matter to be accepted. Rubin used the latest technology developed by Kent Ford which produced detectors with increased sensitivity to measure the spectra of the galaxies. The accuracy of her measurements was enough to convince other astronomers that extra matter was needed. In 2019, Peebles received the Nobel prize for his work on dark matter and much more in cosmology. Despite Rubin's work being recognised as proving dark matter exists, Rubin did not receive a Noble prize.

So why do rotation curves tell us dark matter exists? By looking at the amount of light in a galaxy we can make assumptions about how many stars there are and so determine how much mass it has. Once we know it's mass

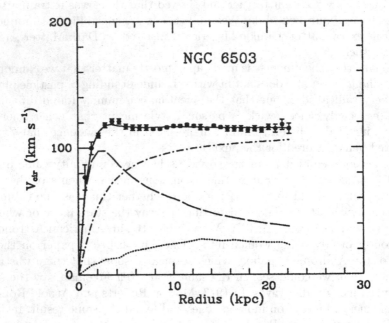

Figure 3.5: Rotation curves for spiral galaxy NGC6503. The rotation velocity is plotted from the centre of the galaxy to the edges (along the radius). The black dots show the measured values, the solid line shows the curve that best fits the measurements when dark matter and matter in the stars are included. If the galaxy consisted of just the matter in the stars then the curve would be the long dashed line. The dot/dash line is the curve needed from the extra dark matter. Credit: From Figure 1 by K.G. Begeman, A.H. Broeils and R.H. Sanders, 1991, "Extended rotation curves of spiral galaxies: dark haloes and modified dynamics", *MNRAS*, 249, 523.

then it is possible to calculate how fast the disc should be spinning by using standard equations of gravity. What we would expect is that as you move from the centre of the galaxy towards the outer edges, the rotation velocity will increase at first quite sharply to reach a peak not too far from the centre and then gradually it will slow down until there is eventually no more galaxy to observe. So the outer edges of the galaxy should spin slowly and the inner part of the galaxy should spin quickly. What the rotation curve shows us is that the inner part of the galaxy does increase it's spin but the outer part does not slow down, it continues to spin at the same rate right up to the observable edge.

The rotation curve for the spiral galaxy NGC6503 is shown in Figure 3.5 produced by K.G. Begeman in 1991 [21]. Spiral galaxies are flat, disc-shaped galaxies with spiral arms like the Milky Way. In a spiral galaxy the stars rotate round the centre. The velocity of the stars can be measured at different points across the galaxy and the velocity calculated from the Doppler shift of the light. The dots show the measured values, the solid line shows the curve that best fits the measurements, and the long dashed line shows the expected curve if only the matter from the stars are included. As you can see they are quite different. The extra dark matter needed to fit the measurements is the dot/dash curve.

In more recent times we have two further pieces of evidence that have only been made possible by improvements in our telescope technology. We can see much clearer (higher resolution) and much further. The first additional clue comes from a technique called gravitational lensing and the second comes from a picture of the Bullet Cluster.

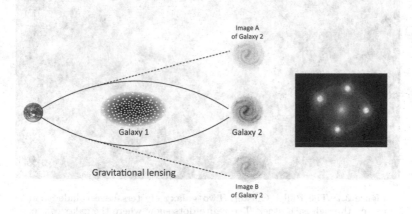

Figure 3.6: Gravitational lensing. The light from galaxy 2 is bent by the gravity of galaxy 1. Galaxy 1 is acting like a lens so that multiple images of galaxy 2 are seen on Earth. The inset shows the four images of galaxy HE 0435-1223 caused by gravitational lensing. Drawing credit: C. Devereux and P. Farrell. Credit: Inset image from Figure 1 by S.H. Suyu, V. Bonvin, F. Courbin, et al, 2017, "HOLiCOW I. H0 Lenses in COSMOGRAIL'S Wellspring: Program Overview", *MNRAS*, 468, 3, 2590.

Gravitational lensing was predicted in 1936 by Albert Einstein when he used his theory of relativity to show that light can be affected by gravity. Just as a glass lens magnifies or distorts an image as it bends light passing through it, an object that is big enough can bend light by gravity attracting the light towards it. This is called gravitational lensing. The object has to be very big to act as a lens and galaxies are objects that are big enough. Gravitational lensing was first observed in 1979 [22], where the galaxy with the catchy name YGKOW G1 was discovered acting as a lens to another galaxy behind it called the Twin Quasar. It is called the Twin Quasar because we see it twice; the gravitational lens creates two images of the quasar. The discovery of the Twin Quasar confirmed Einstein's prediction of gravitational lensing more than 40 years earlier. Figure 3.6 shows how gravitational lensing works along with an image of a lensed galaxy as we see it. The mass of the lensing galaxy can be calculated by analysing the multiple images of the quasar. What is found is that the galaxy has a much bigger mass than the visible light would suggest. This is evidence for dark matter.

Figure 3.7: The Bullet Cluster. Two galaxy clusters have collided and passed through each other. The white dots show where the galaxies are. The cloudy region shows the X-ray image highlighting where the gas is, most of the visible mass is in the gas. The two white X show where the centre of mass is for the two passing galaxies. Most of the mass of the galaxies is in a different place to where the visible mass is. This is strong evidence for dark matter. Credit: X-ray: NASA/CXC/CfA/M.Markevitch, Optical and lensing map: NASA/STScI, Magellan/U.Arizona/D.Clowe, Lensing map: ESO WFI.

There is a more direct piece of evidence for the existence of dark matter. This comes from observations of the Bullet Cluster which is in fact two clusters of galaxies colliding. A picture of the Bullet Cluster is shown in Figure 3.7. The two clusters have hit head on and moved through each other (after-all most of a galaxy and galaxy cluster is space). The galaxies are seen as the bright dots. The cloudy regions are where there is hot gas which is detected from the X-rays that it gives off. Most of the matter in clusters exists as hot gas. The two brightest areas are where the hot gas of the two clusters are. The interesting thing about this picture is that the mass of the two clusters can also be measured using gravitational lensing and what was found is that the places where most of the mass is is not where the gas is [23]. The visible matter in the gas has been separated from the bulk of the mass of the clusters which we cannot see – the dark matter. When the clusters were moving through each other the gas was slowed down by the interactions between particles. Dark matter does not interact so it carried on moving at the same speed. This separated the two types of matter. This picture provides one of the most direct clues for the existence of dark matter.

How much dark matter is in the universe? Our current estimates of dark matter tell us that 85% of the universe is made up of dark matter. So the matter that we know and understand, the matter that we can touch and see on Earth – a chair, a tree, a rock – is only 15% of all the matter that exists in the universe. Dark matter exists here on Earth, it is part of the structure of the Solar System. Potentially, millions of dark matter particles pass through us every second. They don't do anything, they do not interact with us since we are made of normal matter and dark matter does not interact with ordinary matter, but it's interesting to think that dark matter is all around us all of the time. The amount of dark matter in the universe is an important number, it can tell us whether the universe will continue to expand forever or eventually start contracting and become smaller. If there is a large amount of mass in the universe it could be enough for gravity to pull it all together and stop the expansion. If there is not enough mass then the universe will continue to expand forever. At the moment, our measurement of the amount of mass in the universe, including dark matter, is not enough to stop it expanding forever.

3.4   CLUE 3: THE COSMIC MICROWAVE BACKGROUND

Relic light from the Big Bang

In a laboratory in New Jersey in 1964, two young Americans were working on modifying a six metre long horn antenna so that they could detect radio waves coming from the sky. They wanted to look at galaxies and giant gas clouds using the radio signals they give off. This horn antenna would be the most advanced radio telescope of the time and it was optimised to work at a wavelength of 7.35 cm – a microwave. They got the telescope working but they could not get rid of a persistent background noise that would interfere with their measurements. They checked the wiring, cooled the detector with liquid helium, and carefully eliminated all the sources of noise that they could think of, including removing pigeons and their droppings from the inside of the horn. The background noise remained whatever they did and it was the same amount of noise wherever they looked in the sky. The two astronomers were Arno Penzias and Robert Wilson [24] and what they did not know at the time was that they had detected what was to become one of the most important clues for the Big Bang. It is called the Cosmic Microwave Background, shortened to the CMB, and they won the Nobel prize in 1978 for their discovery.

As sometimes happens in science serendipity then played a part. Penzias was explaining the background noise problem to a colleague, Bernard Burke in MIT, who knew about some work by Robert Dicke and James Peebles that predicted just such a signal. Penzias contacted Dicke in Princeton who visited the telescope to see the signal for himself. This was the signal his team had been looking for. Dicke then repeated the measurement at a wavelength of 3.2cm on equipment they had at Princeton. This confirmed the result.

So what do we think the CMB is and why is it's discovery so important? In 1948, George Gamow, Herman Bethe and Ralph Alpherin [25] were studying how the first particles could form just after the Big Bang. The nuclear reactions that had to have taken place required an extremely hot environment and would also have created light at extremely small wavelengths. This light would travel through the universe and eventually be seen by us. The expansion of the universe means that the light would also expand as it travelled, making the wavelength longer (called the cosmological redshift). Gamow had calculated that as this light hits the Earth today it would be the wavelength of microwaves. This is the Cosmic Microwave Background, it is light that was created from nuclear reactions in the hot soup of the early universe, it is a relic of the Big Bang. It is hard to explain the CMB without the Big Bang.

The CMB has a bit more history to it. In the early hot soup after the Big Bang, light would have been scattered by the charged particles that were whizzing around in the then very small universe. If we existed at that time, we would not have been able to see anything just a dense, thick fog. About 380,000 years after the Big Bang this changed. The universe had cooled enough for the charged particles to join together to form atoms. Now the light was not scattered by the atoms and could freely travel through the universe unhindered by the particles. When we look at the CMB light we are looking at the light from that time when atoms formed 13.8 billion years ago. To me, that is incredible.

So when Penzias and Wilson saw a microwave background cosmologists were very excited. This was the CMB they had been searching for 16 years. At that time there was still a debate about whether the universe started with a Big Bang or whether it was unchanging. The discovery of the CMB stopped this debate, the Big Bang was accepted (mostly).

Following it's discovery, there have been three major space-based telescopes observing the CMB each one providing more detail and more information; the NASA *COBE* (COsmic Background Explorer) satellite telescope launched in 1989, the NASA *WMAP* (Wilkinson Microwave Anisotropy Probe) satellite telescope launched in 2001, and the ESA *Planck* satellite telescope launched in 2009.

The top map in Figure 3.8 shows the CMB across the whole of the sky taken with the *COBE* telescope. If you look up at the sky and imagine a sphere around the Earth, take that sphere and unravel it until it is flat then you get the oval map in the picture. As you can see, the signal of the CMB is extremely uniform. It looks the same wherever we look in the sky. This is what Penzias and Wilson saw, it's there but there is not much to look at. The uniformity of the CMB across the whole of the sky is a clue. Any theory of the universe has to explain why the CMB is the same everywhere. We will come back to the other two maps later.

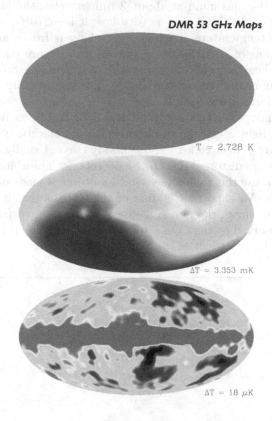

DMR 53 GHz Maps

T = 2.728 K

ΔT = 3.353 mK

ΔT = 18 μK

Figure 3.8: The Cosmic Microwave Background (CMB). Each image shows the whole sky round the Earth. The top image looks the same everywhere and shows the extreme uniformity of the CMB. The middle image shows the 1 in 1,000 differences due to the rotation of the Earth. The bottom image shows the 1 in 100,000 differences that are the fluctuations of the CMB. The central region is blocked out where the Milky Way interferes with the signal. Credit: NASA/COBE.

The existence of the CMB is not the only cosmological clue from it. As it was probed further we saw more detail and got further clues.

The next clue from the CMB comes from it's temperature. This may sound strange that light can have a temperature, but it does. If you look through an infra-red camera you can see the heat coming from an object but what you are looking at is infra-red light. Every object absorbs light and emits light: humans do, a rock does and the Earth does. In theory all objects emit at all wavelengths, but the maximum wavelength will depend on the temperature of the object. The hotter it is the more energy the light has and the maximum is at a smaller wavelength, such as ultra-violet and X-rays. Cooler objects have the maximum at longer wavelengths. The human body radiates infra-red light with a maximum at about 0.01mm wavelength. The CMB is detected as a microwave with the maximum at about 2 mm wavelength. This means that the temperature of the CMB light is very low; it is −270°C, only 3°C above absolute zero, a temperature at which everything is frozen and there is no movement of atoms or particles. As scientists we measure temperature from absolute zero and call a degree of temperature a Kelvin (K). So the CMB light that we see today is at a temperature of 3K. The temperature of the universe when the CMB formed was 3,000K.

An object that perfectly absorbs all the light falling on it and perfectly emits all of that light is called a blackbody. A pure blackbody would give off a unique signature of light called the blackbody curve. Usually, the blackbody curves we detect are distorted due to the objects not absorbing and emitting perfectly. We can use this to analyse what an object is made of by looking at the light it emits. An important finding of the CMB is that it has an almost perfect blackbody curve, the purest we have ever measured (see Figure 3.9). This was first observed by the *COBE* telescope in 1996 [26]. It is an important clue that the CMB is a result of the Big Bang.

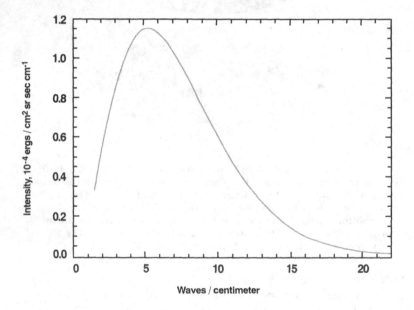

Figure 3.9: The temperature spectrum of the Cosmic Microwave Background (CMB). The solid line is the intensity from a pure black body. The observed data points fit so accurately that they are within the width of the solid line. Credit: NASA/COBE.

The next clue is not so much a Cosmological Clue but one that gives us information about our Solar System and one that we have to take into account when making measurements. It comes from very small changes in the CMB.

When we measure the temperature of the CMB more accurately we start to see very small variations. Some of these temperature differences are caused by noise from objects in the sky, but some of it can tell us more information. The first small variations observed are to do with the Doppler shift of the temperature spectrum. The middle map in Figure 3.8 shows these changes in temperature of a thousandth of a degree, that is 1 part in 1,000. If we look at the sky one way we see the CMB spectrum slightly blueshifted, meaning it is coming towards us, and if we look in the opposite direction in the sky then we see the CMB slightly redshifted, it is moving away from us. What we are seeing is the Doppler shift of the light due to the rotation of the Earth moving relative to the CMB. This 'dipole' as it is called, was first observed by Edward Conklin (1969) [27] and Paul Henry (1971) [28]. The measurement of this dipole allows us to calculate that the Earth moves round the Sun at 30 km/s and the Solar System moves relative to the CMB at 370 km/s. If we remove the rotation of the Solar System round the centre of the Milky Way and the Milky Way round the centre of the Local Group (the group of galaxies that we live in), values we know by other measurements, then we can determine that the Local Group is moving relative to the CMB in the direction of the Hydra constellation at the speed of 630 km/s.

The next Cosmological Clue also comes from even smaller variations in the CMB temperature, changes in temperature of ten millionth of a degree, that is 1 part in 100,000. These fluctuations were predicted by theory [29] and finding them was yet more evidence for the Big Bang. The theory is that the fluctuations are the small changes in the density of matter in the very early universe and the denser areas became the seeds for galaxies forming in the future. The fluctuations in the CMB are shown in the bottom map of Figure 3.8. The lighter and darker areas are the hotter and cooler regions of the CMB temperature. The grey area of the centre strip is where the Milky Way is and it is difficult to see the CMB through it's stars, gas and dust. What we are looking at is the universe as it looked 13.8 billion years ago and we are able to see the regions that grew into galaxies and became the universe that we see today.

The *COBE* telescope was the first measurement of the CMB from space and was sensitive enough to confirm the uniformity of the CMB, measure the near perfect blackbody spectrum, and discover the tiny temperature fluctuations [30]. It was such an important instrument in giving us clues from the CMB that two of the key scientists involved in the mission, John Mather and George Smoot, were awarded the Nobel Prize in 2006.

With measurements from the more recent *Planck* telescope we are learning even more about the CMB and it keeps on giving us more information about the universe. We can measure the Hubble constant which gives us the age of the universe. We can measure how much total matter is in the universe and work out whether it will keep on expanding. We can also use gravitational lensing techniques, just as we can with galaxies, where the CMB is the background light and dark matter is the lensing object, and from this we can make a map of where dark matter exists. We are seeing light that was emitted shortly after the Big Bang and from this light we can measure how quickly the universe is expanding, see dark matter, and confirm that the Big Bang happened. The measurement of the CMB is a triumph of modern science.

3.5   CLUE 4: THE ORIGIN OF THE ELEMENTS

Abundance of Hydrogen and Helium

The fourth Cosmological Clue looks at how the chemical elements formed in the universe. The development of the physics that showed that hydrogen, helium and a small amount of lithium and beryllium, the first four elements of the periodic table, must have formed within minutes of the Big Bang explosion is a vital piece of evidence that the Big Bang happened and it comes from a totally different source than looking at galaxies in the sky. It comes from our understanding of nuclear physics; the study of how protons and neutrons bind together to form the nuclei of atoms. The formation of these light chemical elements following the Big Bang is called Big Bang Nucleosynthesis (BBN).

In the 1940s, scientists around the World were investigating how stars could produce their energy by calculating the possible nuclear reactions that could take place. It was already known that stars were mostly made from hydrogen and that nuclear fusion in stars could combine hydrogen nuclei to make the light elements helium, lithium, carbon, nitrogen and oxygen, from work by Arthur Eddington (British), Hans Bethe (German-American) and Carl von Weizsäcker (German). What was not known is how elements heavier than oxygen could be produced. The British astronomer, Fred Hoyle, was working on this and in 1946 [31] he showed how heavy elements could form in stars. In his paper he stated that "it is shown that a roughly uniform abundance of the elements over the whole of the periodic table can be obtained". It has since been shown that all elements do not occur equally in the universe.

Russian nuclear physicist, George Gamow, and his student Ralph Alpher were working on a different model and in their 1948 paper [32] they proposed that the chemical elements formed in the Big Bang, not stars, and that there would be more light elements than heavy ones. This was quite different than the assumption that elements are equally abundant, the view that had been held up to then. Gamow jovially claims he added the nuclear physicist, Hans Bethe, to the paper just to be able to have the authors written as Alpher, Bethe and Gamow which sounds similar to the first three letters of the Greek alphabet: alpha (α), beta (β), gamma (γ). The paper is now known as the $\alpha\beta\gamma$ paper. There was a flaw in the paper though. It claimed that all the elements could be built up starting from hydrogen which would successively capture neutrons to build up all the other elements. The problem was that stable elements with five and eight nuclear particles do not exist so two rungs on the ladder were broken. It had become apparent that only the lightest four elements, hydrogen, helium, lithium and beryllium could be produced by the Big Bang. So the idea was not accepted. More work was needed.

Hoyle was spurred on; the success of the stellar theory and the shortcomings of the BBN theory led Hoyle to propose the Steady State theory in 1948 [33]. If he could show that stars produce all the elements then maybe the Big Bang was not needed. There are many complex nuclear reactions involved but eventually Hoyle and his colleagues showed that elements from carbon to nickel could be produced in supernovae explosions from dying stars. All the elements, the light and heavy ones, are spread into the universe by the supernova explosions to be used again in new stars. This work was reviewed in a paper by Geoffrey Burbidge, Margaret Burbidge, William Fowler and Hoyle [34]. It showed that light and heavy elements could be produced either in fusion reactions in stars or in supernova explosions of dying stars and added that even heavier elements could be produced by neutron capture processes seeded by the heavy elements from the supernova. This 1957 paper is one of the most widely cited papers in astronomy and is known as the BBFH theory after the authors initials. Fowler received a Nobel prize for this work in 1983.

Despite the success of the BBFH paper, it had a problem with it. There exits a type of hydrogen called deuterium (D) which is one proton and one neutron (normal hydrogen has one proton only). Nuclear physics tells us that deuterium is not produced in nuclear fusion within the stars nor by supernova explosions, in fact stars destroy it. So if all the elements are produced only by stars then there should be no deuterium in the universe. But there is. About 0.01% of all the elements in the universe is deuterium. So where did this come from? There was also another problem which was not known at the time. It predicts an abundance of helium of about 4% but what we measure is an abundance of 25% throughout the universe.

The problems with the stellar theory now spurred Gamow and other scientists to prove the BBN theory. This included Hoyle [35] who, in trying to disprove BBN, showed that it would create 24% of helium, the value that was later shown to be correct. Once the neutron capture approach was dropped, improvements in the understanding of nuclear physics eventually enabled the abundance of the elements to be correctly calculated from BBN. The BBN theory as it stands today goes like this. When the universe was 1 second old it was at a temperature of 10 billion degrees. Before this the universe was even hotter and the protons and neutrons formed. After 1 second the universe had cooled enough that the protons and neutrons started to bind together to form small nuclei. There was also a lot of very high energy light around at that time which collided with the nuclei and broke them up. So elements were constantly forming and splitting apart in nuclear reactions.

When the universe was 3 minutes old the temperature had dropped to 1 billion degrees and now the nuclear reactions had stopped and whatever nuclei existed at that time remained, they were no longer broken up. Between the times of 1 second to 3 minutes there was another process going on. When neutrons are a free particle (not bound in a nucleus) they decay and turn into protons. This is at a rate of 620 seconds for half the neutrons to decay into protons (the half-life). When the neutrons are bound into a nucleus they stop decaying and are stable. We can calculate how many neutrons would have decayed into protons during this period. What we find is that after 3 minutes there was one neutron to every seven protons. Every neutron combined with a proton to form an element. The most stable of the elements that formed were deuterium (1p+1n), helium 3 (2p+1n), helium 4 (2p+2n), lithium 6 (3p+3n) and lithium 7 (3p+4n) (note that there is no element with five particles).

Unlike neutrons, protons do not decay as free particles, so once all the neutrons bound with a proton to form elements then there were still plenty of protons left that had no neutrons to bind with. These protons are the hydrogen that exists today in the universe. We can calculate how much there is of each element relative to the amount of protons left on their own (hydrogen). About 8% of nuclei are helium and most of the rest hydrogen with a trace of other elements. We normally quote these figures by the mass of the elements and since helium is heavier than hydrogen we find that the universe, when it is just a few minutes old, had fixed the elements to be (by mass) 75% hydrogen, 25% helium, 0.01% deuterium and 0.00000001% lithium (and even smaller amounts of beryllium).

Today, the accepted theory for how the chemical elements formed in the universe is a mixture of both the Big Bang Nucleosynthesis and stellar synthesis. The Big Bang produced 24.67% helium and 75.32% hydrogen with tiny traces of deuterium, lithium and beryllium. Stellar synthesis produces all the other elements by nuclear fusion in the stars and in supernovae explosions of dying stars. Today, all the elements, other than hydrogen and helium, make up less than 2% of the elements in the universe.

So far we have looked at the theory of the abundance of the elements but to make it a Cosmological Clue we need observational evidence. So how do we measure the abundance of the elements? We want to measure the abundance close to the Big Bang, the primordial abundance, because the fusion in stars and supernova explosions produce more elements and will have changed the balance. What we look for is a gas cloud that has no stars in it and low levels of heavy elements and we assume that this cloud is similar in it's characteristics to a primordial cloud, it has not been contaminated by stars. If we shine a light through the cloud we can determine the elements that exist in the cloud by looking at the light coming through it. A suitable light is a quasar, which is a very bright star, and if we find one that sits behind the gas cloud we can use it to measure the abundances of the elements. We look at specific wavelengths of the light that is coming through the cloud where we know that hydrogen, helium and deuterium absorb the light. By comparing how much light is absorbed at these wavelengths we can calculate the ratio of helium and deuterium to hydrogen. The value obtained is 25% for helium [36] and 0.003%, for deuterium. Since deuterium is destroyed in stars, then seeing any deuterium at all is evidence for the Big Bang. The observed value of helium matches the amount that the BBN theory predicts. For comparison, in the

Sun there is about 28% helium and virtually no deuterium, which is consistent with stars producing helium and destroying deuterium.

This is strong evidence. The Big Bang Nucleosynthesis theory predicts exactly the amount of light elements there are in the universe, and the theory of nuclear reactions in stars gives the wrong amount. The BBN Cosmological Clue also shows us something about how science is done. Having two different theories, BBN and production in stars, spurred scientists on; it pushed them to fully explore, explain and evidence their proposals and in doing so kept pushing the boundaries of science.

3.6   CLUE 5: THE COSMIC WEB

The large-scale structure of the universe

Since Hubble showed in 1924 that the universe contained many galaxies, it was thought that galaxies were randomly spread out over the universe. This is not what we observe. Where galaxies exist has a structure to it. It looks like a giant three-dimensional spiders web and we call it the cosmic web, it is the large-scale structure of the universe. A picture of the cosmic web is shown in Figure 3.10 and it's production is yet another amazing achievement by astronomers. Each dark dot in the picture is a galaxy. There are over 220,000 galaxies of different sizes, shapes, types and brightness, some are in groups and clusters, some are alone, and together they make up a pattern that is another Cosmological Clue. This picture was produced in 2001 by the Two Degree Field Galaxy Redshift Survey (2dFGRS) based at the Anglo-Australian telescope in New South Wales, Australia [37]. It covers two patches of sky (the two lobes of the picture) with the Earth at the centre of the picture and it shows the galaxies at increasing distance from the Earth. The most distant galaxies are at the edge of the image and are more difficult to detect so we only see the brightest ones. In the image it looks like there are less galaxies at the edges, although there are probably the same number but we are seeing less of them due to the limits of what we can detect.

What we see in the cosmic web picture is galaxies clumping together into clusters with filaments that connect the clusters into superclusters. About 90% of galaxies live in the filaments and clusters. These structures are on a massive scale – millions of light-years. The long, large sheet-like structures of the densest regions of galaxies are called walls, the smaller walls are called sheets. The largest walls are called great walls, we have only seen about five or six of these in the whole universe. The first great wall to be observed was the Coma Wall in 1989 [38]; it is about 500 million light-years long, 200 million light-years wide and 15 million light-years thick. The largest structure in the universe is the Hercules–Corona Borealis Great Wall, found in 2013 [39], and is 10 billion light-years long. There are also 'voids': places where there are not many galaxies. The Milky Way lives next to a void called the Keenan, Barger, and Cowie Void (KBC) named after the astronomers who studied it

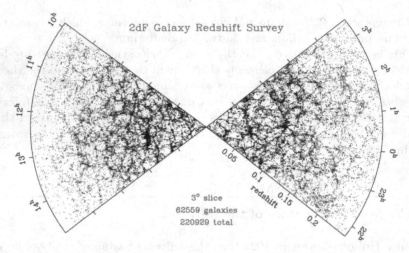

Figure 3.10: Picture of the cosmic web as observed by the 2dF Galaxy Redshift Survey. Each dark dot in the picture is a galaxy. There are over 220,000 galaxies. The Earth is at the centre of the picture and it shows the galaxies at increasing distance from the Earth. Credit: From Figure 18 by M. Colless, G. Dalton, S. Maddox, et al, 2001, "The 2dF Galaxy Redshift Survey: spectra and redshifts", *MNRAS*, 328, 1039.

in 2013 [40]. It is about 2 billion light-years in diameter and is the largest void observed. It is also known as the Local Hole. Typically voids are about 100 million light-years across and they make up about 90% of the universe.

When we look at the universe over a distance of 10 million light-years we may see some galaxies. If we look at a different piece of the universe over the same distance we will see a different number of galaxies in different positions; sometimes there may be lots of galaxies (if we are looking at a cluster), sometimes none. If we increase this distance (zooming out) to 100 million light-years then we see the galaxies merged as the cosmic web: the clusters, filaments, walls and voids. As we look around at a different piece of the universe then it will look different depending on whether we are looking at a void, or wall or cluster. As we zoom out even further and make this piece of the universe even bigger, up to 300 million light-years diameter, then these differences disappear, each piece now looks similar. The exact details are different, but they all have similar amounts of galaxies and filaments and voids in them. This is the size at which the universe becomes uniform: 300 million light-years. That the universe has a size at which it is uniform is considered to be a fundamental rule; the cosmological principle – the universe has no special place and looks the same wherever you are. This is only true on the scale of 300 million light-years.

The first observation of the cosmic web was by Valérie de Lapparent, Margaret Geller and John Huchra in 1986 [41]. They plotted a map of 11,00 galaxies, from the CfA Redshift Survey, showing the distance and position of each galaxy relative to the Earth. They found that the galaxies were not randomly placed. Others before them had seen massive voids and superstructures but they had not realised they are part of a larger structure. By chance, the slice of galaxies of the CfA map shows the clusters and filaments looking a little like Leonardo Da Vinci's drawing of Vitruvian Man.

The discovery of the cosmic web in 1986 caused problems for the theory of how galaxies and structure formed following the Big Bang. Such large voids and superclusters were not predicted by the theory. Once again James Peebles played an important role in yet another clue. He was one of the early researchers on the theory of how galaxies and the cosmic web could form and led the way in using the Standard Model to build the theoretical framework for structure formation [42]. This is yet another topic that he received the Nobel prize for in 2019.

The theory of how galaxies and large-scale structure formed is based on the competing processes of gravity pushing matter together and the expansion of the universe pulling matter apart. It starts in the very early universe when matter is a uniform soup of particles. If it was totally uniform then nothing else would have happened and the universe would still be a uniform soup of particles today. There needed to be some small variations in the density of the particle soup to act as gravity seeds to produce future stars and galaxies. Where these seeds could have come from we do not know; it is speculated that they came from quantum fluctuations but it remains one of the Cosmological Problems. Some of the slightly denser regions would have had enough gravity to overcome the expansion of the universe and allow the particles in the region to start collapsing together. The particles slowly clumped together which increased their gravitational attraction, this pulled in more particles, increasing gravity to pull in even more particles, until there were enough particles close enough to bind together to form stars. Over time, gravity pulled the stars together into groups of stars and, when there were enough of them, it became a galaxy. Galaxies then attracted other galaxies forming clusters of galaxies.

So where do the filaments of the cosmic web come from? This is where dark matter comes in. We find that there is not enough atomic matter for gravity to overcome the expansion of the universe and form stars. Much more matter is needed; 85% more. This is the dark matter. It provides enough gravity for dark matter clumps to form. The atomic matter is attracted to these dark matter clumps, allowing stars and galaxies to form. Where the stars and galaxies form is determined by where the dark matter is; it is the scaffold for the stars to form in. The picture of the cosmic web is the picture of where dark matter is in the universe today and it also shows us how the peaks and troughs of dark matter was distributed in the early universe.

What about the voids? The gravitational collapse of matter into galaxies will have produced voids as matter was attracted out of the less dense regions into the more dense regions. This is not the whole story though. The voids produced this way would be limited in size and we have seen that there are some big voids in the universe. The big voids come from the early universe where there were less dense regions in the primordial soup of particles. It is these less dense regions that grow to become the massive voids. The expansion of the universe increases the size of voids. To fully explain the structure of the voids in the cosmic web we need to add dark energy to our theories which speeds up the expansion in the later universe.

How can we test our theories of structure formation? We cannot do experiments with the universe, we only have one universe to look at and we can't change it to try out different universes. So what do we do? We use computers to create simulations of different universes and compare the results with our observations. When I say different universes I mean different models: some with dark matter and no dark energy, some with dark energy and no dark matter, we can vary the amount of atomic matter and dark matter, we can vary how quickly the universe expands and vary how strong dark energy is. Each model will produce a universe that looks different, has a different number of galaxies, filament shapes, sizes of galaxy clusters, and we can then see if any of them match what we observe. It is only in the last 30 years that we have had the computing power to do this and it has opened up a whole new way of researching cosmology. The ability to test theories using computers means that we can be more precise with our theories and, by using new technology in increasingly powerful telescopes, we can also be more precise with our observations. We live in the age of 'precision cosmology'.

A computer simulation calculates just a section of the universe, enough to show us how the cosmic web would look. It starts by having particles of matter in a box. It adds the laws of gravity that apply to the dark matter particles and atomic matter, and it adds the rules of collisions that take place between the atomic matter particles (dark matter does not interact). It adds expansion of space and acceleration of the expansion. It then calculates where each group of particles will move with time, step by step, so that at any point the simulation can be stopped and we can look at what the universe looks like at that time. When the simulation reaches today's time it stops. Then we compare the computer models with the observed cosmic web to see which ones look the same and which ones don't.

The result of a simulation by the Millennium team in 2005 is shown in Figure 3.11. When compared to the observed cosmic web from 2dFGRS (Figure 3.10) the two pictures look very similar. It was found [43] that to reproduce the cosmic web to match the observed picture then dark matter needed to be 'cold' rather than 'hot'. By hot we mean that it is travelling near the speed of light, and cold means that it is much less than the speed of light, possibly as slow as 50 m/s [44]. The computer simulations that use cold dark matter closely fit how the cosmic web looks, it has the fine structure and filaments in it that we observe. If we use simulations that are based on hot dark matter then we still get a cosmic web, it has the basic larger filaments and clusters but not the detailed fine structure (see Figure 5.1). This is evidence that dark matter is cold.

125 Mpc/h

Figure 3.11: Computer simulations of the cosmic web, using the ΛCDM model, showing a similar spider's web pattern to the observed cosmic web. Each white dot is a galaxy. Simulation from the Millennium team. Credit: From Figure 1 by V. Springel, S.D.M. White, A. Jenkins, et al, 2005, "Simulations of the formation, evolution and clustering of galaxies and quasars", *Nature*, 435, 629.

Our observation of the cosmic web is a Cosmological Clue. Any cosmology theory must be able to explain why it is there and why it looks like it does. From the theoretical work of Peebles and others, and the use of computer simulations, we can test the Standard Model to reproduce the cosmic web as it looks today. The cosmic web tells us about how structure formed in the universe, that dark matter must exist and must be cold rather than hot, and about the expansion of the universe including the need for dark energy acceleration. One Cosmological Clue gives us evidence for the whole Standard Model of Cosmology.

3.7   CLUE 6: THE EXISTENCE OF DARK ENERGY

The expanding universe is accelerating

The discovery of dark energy in 1998 is the most recent Cosmological Clue. Dark energy is even stranger than dark matter. We do not know what it is, we do not even know how it can exist, but the evidence is that it is there. The evidence for dark energy is strong enough that we include it in our Standard Model of Cosmology. So what is this last Cosmological Clue?

The discovery of dark energy was the discovery that the expansion of the universe is accelerating, it is getting bigger, faster. It was found by two teams that were looking for the opposite effect; the universe should have been slowing down. The predicted deceleration came by gravitational braking from dark matter pulling the universe inwards. In 1979, it had been suggested by Stirling Colgate [45] that distant supernova could measure the deceleration. By the 1990s, technology had advanced enough to be able to detect distant supernova and the teams set about finding and measuring them. The Supernova Cosmology Project was put together in 1990 by the American, Saul Perlmutter. The second team, the High-z Supernova Team, started their search in 1995 and was set up by the Australian, Brian Schimdt, and his American colleague, Adam Riess. All three astronomers received the Nobel prize in 2011. Why were supernova used? A supernova allows us to measure it's distance further and more accurately than other types of objects in the sky. A supernova is the explosion of a dying star, producing extreme energies so that a single supernova is temporarily as bright as 4 billion Suns. It takes time for light to travel to us from an object, that means that the light we are seeing from a supernova today was emitted in the past. We are seeing a time machine and can look back into the early universe. We are able to see supernova that exploded over 9 billion years ago and can use this to measure the expansion of the universe in the past and compare it to the expansion today. The further away we can make the measurements then the bigger any difference in expansion will be.

A Type Ia supernova starts with a pair of stars that are orbiting each other (binary stars). One of them is a white dwarf (a star that is almost at the end of it's life) which pulls away material from the other star and grows in mass. When the white dwarf reaches a certain size then it will start burning carbon. We know how big the star must be to burn carbon and we know how brightly it will burn at that size, so we can calculate the true brightness of the supernova. All Type 1a supernova have the same brightness and we can use that to measure it's distance. For this reason we call Type 1a supernova 'standard candles'.

The difficulty with measuring supernova is that they only shine brightly for a short period of time, a few weeks, so finding them is tricky and finding faint, distant supernova is even trickier. To show how difficult they are to find, Zwicky took 50 years to find 120 nearby supernovae and a Danish group spent 2 years to find one distant supernova [46].

The High-z Supernova Team made measurements on 50 supernovae: 16 at large distances (looking back to an age between 3 and 8 billion years ago) and 34 that are closer (up to about 1 billion years). They plotted the distance against the brightness of the 50 objects to look for the deceleration of the expanding universe. They were expecting the gradient of the line to slowly decrease as the distance increased. To their surprise the gradient increased. The more distant supernova were further away than they should have been by 10–15%. This was the moment that dark energy was discovered. To start with the team was sceptical of the result. They checked for any errors in the equipment or measurements, and double-checked the possibility that dust could be dimming their supernova, or that the supernova may be dimmer in the past, evolving in a different way than expected. They even looked at the influence of the Local Hole, the void in the cosmic web surrounding the Milky Way. But the results held out. They slowly realised the importance of their discovery, and then they worked rapidly to get their results published before the other team, sending it to the publisher on 13 March 1998 [47].

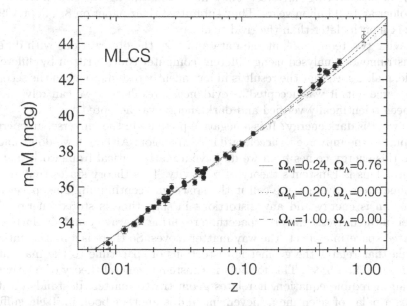

Figure 3.12: Distance of supernovae plotted against their brightness (m-M). The top solid line is the prediction from ΛCDM including dark energy. The other lines are predictions with no dark energy. Credit: From Figure 4 by A.G. Riess, A.V. Filippenko, P. Challis, et al, 1998, "Observational evidence from supernovae for an accelerating universe and a cosmological constant", *Astronomical Journal*, 116, 1009.

The graph that they presented in their paper is shown in Figure 3.12. The distance is given in units of redshift (z) and the brightness is given in units of magnitude (mag). Each point on the graph is a measurement of a single supernova. The small lines on each point show the possible error in the measurement. The straight lines in the graph show the theoretical line that the supernova would be expected to fit in three different models of the universe. The bottom (dashed) line is the universe with no dark energy and the top (solid) line is the universe with dark energy included. What the graph shows is that the supernova at large distances group towards the top line, the model with dark energy included. This is the evidence for dark energy.

Another piece of information that can be gained from this graph is the age of the universe. If the universe is expanding quicker now then it must have been expanding slower in the past making our age estimates too low. From their results, the High-z Supernova Team estimated a new age for the universe of 14.2 billion years.

At the same time the Supernova Cosmology Project was also finding and measuring supernova, and within a few months of Riess' paper published their results [48]. They measured 42 supernova up to similar distances and also found an accelerating universe. They measured the age of the universe as even older at 14.9 billion years. They submitted their paper on 8th Sept 1998, only six months later than the rival team.

Having two teams look at the data and take the observations with different instruments, analysed using different computer codes written by different people, makes sure that the result is independently tested. So when the second result came out, it was accepted as evidence, a result that we can rely on. It had been scientifically verified and dark energy was accepted.

So what is dark energy? It is a negative pressure in the universe, an energy that pushes the universe to accelerate it's expansion. Although we don't know where this energy comes from we do have a mathematical framework that it fits into. This is Einstein's theory of relativity. This theory states that space and time are equivalent, we call it the spacetime continuum. The spacetime continuum is energy and any distortions in spacetime is stored energy. All matter in the universe distorts spacetime resulting in gravity and similarly the distorted spacetime affects the way matter moves. So there is a mathematical formula that relates the geometric distortions of spacetime to the mass and movement of an object. This formula is Einstein's general theory of relativity. It is an incredible equation, it relates geometry to matter. It stands on it's own as a pillar of scientific achievement and is another book in itself, suffice it to say that it has observational evidence that confirms the theory and is fundamental to the mathematics of cosmology. (Note that the special theory of relativity is the famous $E = mc^2$ equation and provides the speed limit of the universe; nothing can travel faster than light.)

When Einstein first developed his formula in 1915 he wanted to show that the universe was static, the steady state. What he found though, was that to make the universe static he had to add another term into his equation which he called the cosmological constant, Λ. There was no physical equivalence of this constant but it made the maths work. Einstein was not comfortable adding it but he accepted it. When Hubble showed that the universe was expanding in 1929, Einstein had to reject the cosmological constant and took it out of his formula. He described adding it as his 'biggest blunder'. The discovery of dark energy means that we need to put the cosmological constant back into the equation in order to make the universe accelerate. We can now relate dark energy to be the cosmological constant, Λ. I'm not sure how Einstein would feel about this.

Amazingly, when we calculate how much dark energy there is it comes to 70% of all energy in the universe. This includes the energy that makes up all the elements and all the dark matter. That means most of what exists in the universe is dark energy; and we didn't even know it was there until 1998! We have a few ideas as to what dark energy might be. It could be to do with fluctuations in the spacetime continuum at extremely small scales, at the quantum level, a size that is smaller than even the smallest sub-atomic particles. This quantum energy in the spacetime continuum is called the vacuum energy. Ideas about what the vacuum energy is, and how big it is, are often linked to dark energy. These are speculative ideas, but these speculations are the seeds of future theories.

The way that we present the value of dark energy is as a ratio of the negative pressure that it exerts on the universe relative to the energy density it has (the energy in each unit of volume). This is called the equation of state, w, and tells us how big the acceleration boost is. As the boost gets bigger it increases the dark energy density keeping the ratio the same (a constant). This is one of the strangest things about dark energy; as the universe expands the energy density stays the same, dark energy is being created. The more the universe expands, the more dark energy there is. We do not know how to explain this in terms of what this physically could be, except to say that it is the cosmological constant in Einstein's equation of relativity. As scientists we live with this unknown and are working to understand it. Our current measured value of w is -1. Since w is -1 in the past as well then we could expect it to stay at -1 in the future and that tells us that the universe will expand forever.

The idea of an accelerating universe is not new, it was first proposed by Lemaître in 1931 [49]. It took nearly 70 years for his idea to be shown to be correct. Once again Lemaître appears to be the forgotten scientist. Since it's discovery, the effects of dark energy have been detected using other methods including using the Cosmic Microwave Background, the large-scale structure of the universe and gravitational lensing. It has also been verified with supernova at even greater distances using the *Hubble Space Telescope* with another 135 new supernova found, measured in only 3 years, and over 25 of them from over 9 billion years ago [50, 51]. These supernova also confirm that dark energy is there. The discovery of dark energy is a story of two teams competing to get to the truth, and the truth was not what they expected. Having independent teams discovering the same result, and reaching the same conclusion, confirmed that the acceleration of the universe is a Cosmological Clue.

CHAPTER 4

The Theories

What are the ideas that can explain the Cosmological Clues?
The Scientific Process: INTERPRETATION

4.1 WHAT IS A THEORY?

A theory is an in-depth explanation of why something behaves as it does that has been extensively tested. Any theory of how the universe works has to be able to explain the observations that make up the six Cosmological Clues: galaxies moving away from us, galaxies uniformly rotating to their edges, uniform microwave light across the sky, helium being 25% of the elements, galaxies forming a cosmic web, and supernova seeming more distant than they should. We have seen the evidence for the Cosmological Clues in Chapter 3, now we have to explain them.

What theories do we have that could explain these Cosmological Clues? There seem to be many ideas around. Some are accepted ideas with evidence, some are more speculative ideas that require some evidence. This chapter explains some of the key ideas and identifies which are which. I will not discuss all the ideas because there are quite a few but mostly they are variations on the themes that will be discussed here.

The main theory is the generally accepted 'Standard Model of Cosmology' called the ΛCDM model, read as lambda cold dark matter. Historically, the main rival theory to ΛCDM is the not so accepted 'Steady State Theory'. In science a model is not the same as a theory. A model is a tool to help aid our thinking about how the World works and is used in the daily work of scientists so that over time and with more evidence the model can be built up into a theory that is fully tested. Our cosmology theories are really scientific models because they cannot explain all the evidence and have not been fully tested. You will see in this chapter that the models are detailed and scientifically rigorous and do fit large parts of the evidence, but there are some gaps and unknowns which I will highlight.

The main addition to the ΛCDM model is inflation - the idea that the universe expanded rapidly just after the Big Bang. It has not been accepted as part of the ΛCDM because there has been no evidence for it, but the working assumption of astronomers is that it happened because the theory gets rid of some important Cosmological Problems: the Horizon Problem and the Flatness Problem. It also explains why the universe is expanding and solves a problem from particle physics called the monopole problem. Inflation modifies ΛCDM by adding a massive expansion in the very early universe.

A way of altering the ΛCDM model is to change the laws of gravity so that it is not necessary to introduce unknown dark matter. Although this can explain some of the Cosmological Clues, changing the tried and tested fundamental laws of gravity is not something that is very popular with most scientists. There are many ways the laws can be changed, so there exist a variety of different modified gravity models, I will discuss the basic ideas here.

Then there are the more imaginative ideas: the multiverses, string theory and quantum gravity. This is when the number of ideas really increases. These are speculative ideas that so far have no observational evidence, although there are mathematical frameworks for them. It is the beauty of the equations that spur scientists on in this field, as well as the potential big prize of being able to explain how all of physics and the universe fit together: the 'Life, Universe and Everything' prize (to paraphrase Douglas Adams). I will give a brief overview of these alternative universes, enough so you can see how they fit into cosmology and relate to the six Cosmological Clues.

4.2 THE STANDARD MODEL OF COSMOLOGY

The Lambda Cold Dark Matter Model (ΛCDM)

The Standard Model of Cosmology is not just about the Big Bang, dark matter and dark energy. It is much more. It can explain how matter forms into stars, galaxies and the cosmic web, it has a set of measurable factors that define the model, it is based on the mathematics of the laws of physics, and it can explain our observations of the Cosmic Microwave Background, galaxies moving away from us, and the elements in the universe. It is a powerful model but it also has it's problems; there are things it does not explain and it has introduced dark secrets.

4.2.1 Overview of ΛCDM: From 0 to 14 Billion Years

The Standard Model of Cosmology is called the ΛCDM. The Λ is the Greek symbol for Lambda and represents dark energy and the CDM stands for Cold Dark Matter, two key ingredients of the model. The basic assumption of the model is that it started with an extremely hot, Big Bang explosion and from then on the universe expanded and cooled. This section will give an overview of the model, describing the important events, starting from the Big Bang and moving forwards in time up to the present day. (Figure 1.1 provides a pictorial overview.)

The universe started as a single point. All the energy that exists in the universe today existed at this point. We do not know how this can happen, our laws of physics break down for such a point, but conceptually that is how we think of it. In physics we call such a point a singularity: a point that has an infinite amount of energy and is infinitely small. As scientists we do not like singularities, and normally avoid them, but we do not know how else to describe the start of the universe so we put up with it until we find something better.

About fourteen billion years ago, the singularity changed and created spacetime. The energy released was so massive that it made space and time expand and it continues to expand today. As it expanded the universe started to cool: a universe double the size has half the temperature. This process of cooling is essential to ΛCDM, it is the cooling process that allows different physical processes to happen at different temperatures which manifests itself in the universe changing and evolving.

The ΛCDM story started when the universe was one second old and the temperature was ten billion degrees, about 1,000 times the temperature at the centre of the Sun. It's size was a few light-years across which is a bit less than the distance to our nearest star (Proxima Centuari). Most of the energy in the universe was in the form of light, with the rest of the energy being in small, fundamental particles mainly protons, neutrons, electrons and positrons (the electron's antimatter). They were colliding, annihilating and reforming with each other. It was a cosmic soup of charged particles and light. The universe was a dense, thick fog caused by the light being randomly scattered by the collisions with the charged particles. It is at one second old that one of our Cosmological Clues becomes relevant; Big Bang Nucleosynthesis. This is when protons and neutrons started to combine to form the nuclei of simple chemical elements: helium, deuterium, lithium and beryllium.

By 3 minutes old, the universe had cooled to 1 billion degrees and had grown to a few hundred light-years across. The positrons had virtually all been annihilated leaving mainly electrons, and the nuclei had finished forming since all the neutrons had combined with the protons. There were more protons than neutrons so the universe was left with 75% protons (which is hydrogen), 25% helium (two protons and two neutrons) and traces of the remaining elements. This matches the proportion of the elements that we see in the universe today.

The universe continued to cool but it was another 380,000 years before our next interesting event happened when the universe was at 3,000 degrees. This was when electrons combined with the nuclei of the elements to form atoms, a process called recombination. Atoms have no charge, the negatively charged electrons cancel out the charge of the positively charged protons. Light is not scattered by neutral atoms so it continued in a straight line in whatever direction it was going when recombination happened. The fog in the universe had now cleared. This is now our next Cosmological Clue because this light is what we see today as the Cosmic Microwave Background. The time it took for the CMB to form is called the 'Epoch of Recombination'.

What followed next is the called the Dark Ages. Nothing eventful happened. Just slow gravitational attraction of particles gently moving towards each other. There were no sources of light. The CMB light continued to travel through the universe. This went on for several hundred million years.

Then the first light of the first stars started to appear. It had taken several hundred million years for enough particles to collapse together into a dense ball so that they heated up to over ten million degrees and started reacting with each other to produce nuclear fusion. The result of the fusion was that light, heat and energy was given off by the stars. The dark ages were over. Light was being created in the universe again in a cosmic dawn.

The first stars are likely to have been very big, a few hundred times more massive than the Sun. The biggest stars have the shortest life and after a few million years some of the largest stars will have started to die in supernova explosions leaving behind neutron stars and black holes. In these explosions heavy elements were produced and spread back out into the universe. These heavier elements were themselves pulled together by gravity, along with the lighter elements, to form new second generation stars. The heavier elements allowed smaller stars to form that can live much longer. The Sun is a second generation star and has a lifetime of 12 billion years. The smallest stars, a tenth of the mass of the Sun, can live 1,000 billion years, much longer than the age of the universe today.

An important consequence of stars appearing in the universe was that they gave out ultra-violet (UV) light and the massive first stars would have given out a lot of strong UV light. The UV light affected the atoms surrounding the stars by stripping off electrons in what is called 'ionisation'. The atoms became charged. Now the high energy light was no longer absorbed and all wavelengths of light could travel through space unimpeded. The universe became visible as we see it today. This process is called 'reionisation'. The reionisation happened slowly, appearing first around the stars in bubbles, with more and more bubbles appearing until all the universe was reionised. It took about one billion years for all the hydrogen to be ionised and is called the 'Epoch of Reionisation'. The galaxies we see today contain significant amounts of ionised hydrogen, there is 1 neutral hydrogen to every 10,000 ionised hydrogen atoms.

As the stars were forming, gravity continued to pull them together to form galaxies. The earliest galaxies formed at about a billion years and were irregular shaped and small. As they merged, they grew until they became the smooth, large galaxies of today. At the centre of galaxies black holes formed (or already existed), they attracted more matter and the energy from matter falling into the black holes produced 'active galactic nuclei' that ejected vast amounts of energy, heating up the galaxies and stopping stars from forming. The matter thrown out into the space between the galaxies (the interstellar medium) would fall back to be used again. The space between stars is not empty, it contains the gas, dust and molecules that form future stars.

The newly formed galaxies very slowly started to gather into groups and clusters. This process has taken so long that even the first clusters are still in the process of forming today.

At about 3.5 billion years old star formation was at it's peak, the cosmic noon.

At 9 billion years the Solar System formed, with the Sun and the planets forming at the same time. Earth began.

At 10 billion years life started on Earth.

At 11.5 billion years the effects of dark energy started to dominate and expansion started to accelerate.

Today we are at 13.8 billion years from the Big Bang. The ancestors of humans appeared on Earth about 6 million years ago and it was a mere 200,000 years ago that humans appeared. The telescope was invented 400 years ago and the modern computer 50 years ago and today satellite telescopes and supercomputers allow us to look at the skies and work out how the universe formed.

4.2.2   Early Structure Formation

What about the cosmic web, where does that come into the model? This is where dark matter comes in. To understand the role of dark matter in the formation of stars, galaxies and the cosmic web we need to go back to the beginning, to before protons and neutrons formed, before there were any particles, when the universe was a mere 10^{-35} seconds old (that is 0.000...(30 more zeros)...001 of a second). This is when we speculate that quantum fluctuations appeared. These were the tiniest of tiny spontaneous changes in the spacetime continuum. These are what we assume were the seeds of all the structure we see today, the slightly denser regions that went on to form the stars and galaxies and the cosmic web. Although, we don't really know what seeded the structure so this is our best guess at the moment.

We now go forwards 1 second. This is when nuclei were just beginning to form. We will look at the period from when the universe was 1 second old until it was 380,000 years old when the Cosmic Microwave Background formed. During this time, the role of dark matter in the formation of the cosmic web is crucial but also complicated.

Between the ages of 1 second and 380,000 years, the universe had particles of atomic matter, dark matter, and light randomly moving around, colliding and scattering in all directions. There were regions that were slightly denser (from the early quantum fluctuations) giving them slightly more gravity than the surrounding regions and slowly these denser regions attracted particles towards them. The bigger, denser regions grew faster than the smaller, less dense regions. The dark matter and atomic matter were attracted towards each other by gravity. At the same time an opposite force was also acting on only the atomic matter; it was colliding with light and being scattered out of the denser regions (see Figure 4.1). Let's look at just one region: matter

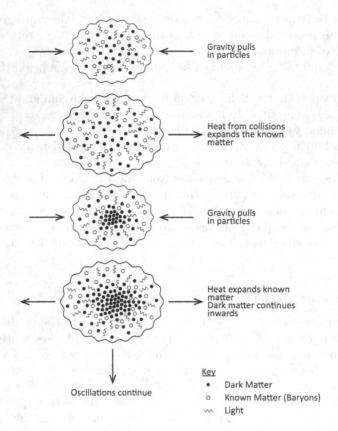

Figure 4.1: Baryonic Acoustic Oscillations. The competing processes of gravity pulling matter inwards, and the collisions of light with atomic matter heating up and pushing outwards, cause oscillations in the early universe called baryonic acoustic oscillations. The result is that dark matter continues to be pulled inwards by gravity but the atomic matter exists in shells around the dark matter. Credit: C.Devereux and P. Farrell.

was moving inwards from gravity, which brought the light and atomic matter closer together, this made them collide more and the region heated up. A hotter region created an outward pressure which expanded the region and it cooled down. As it cooled, gravity could then take hold and pull the region inwards again which heated it up. The region pulsed inwards and outwards in oscillations.

An important property of dark matter is that it does not interact with light or atomic matter and so was not expanded outwards. So while the atomic matter was heating and cooling, the dark matter continued to gravitate inwards forming a core of dark matter surrounded by a pulsating sphere of atomic matter and light. In addition, there was another force acting on the region and that was the pull due to the expansion of the universe. There had to be enough total matter in the region for gravity to overcome this expansion force. So only the densest regions would have formed into dark matter cores, the rest would have expanded away. The dark matter cores attracted more matter and grew bigger, which attracted even more matter getting bigger still; the dense regions got denser.

The dense regions continued to pulse and get denser until the light escaped and left the region. This happened when the universe was 380,000 years old at which time the electrons combined with nuclei to form atoms. The combined electrons and nuclei formed atoms with no charge and these neutral atoms no longer collided with light, the atomic matter was not heated up and the oscillations stopped. The atomic matter close to the dark matter cores could now gravitate inwards. A lot of matter now existed in the central areas of the regions but some of the atomic matter was left further away from the core in a ring around the core and it didn't move inwards. In fact it moved a little further outwards as it was dragged away by the escaping light until it eventually separated from the light and came to a halt. These rings of atomic matter then attracted the dark matter and also grew.

So what was left was a structure of matter that formed from a combination of the denser regions and the rings left over from the oscillations. The structure is mostly dark matter, which is why we say that dark matter is the scaffold of the cosmic web, and over time the atomic matter and dark matter gravitated towards each other to eventually form the universe as we see it today.

Now this may sound a little speculative since it was in the very early universe so how can we know that these tiny regions were oscillating in this way? Well, we can see them today. Amazingly, there are two very different ways that we can see them.

When the oscillations stopped, some were at a maximum stretch, some were at a maximum compression, and the rest were somewhere in between. This froze into a pattern, a little like a three-dimensional version of the pattern raindrops make on water. The pattern is now seen in where galaxies exist in the universe and I'll come back to this later.

The other place that the pattern is seen is in the light that escaped from the regions. This light continued unimpeded throughout the rest of the life of the universe and we can see it today. This is the light of the Cosmic Microwave Background. The pattern of the oscillating regions is embedded in the CMB light in small fluctuations in the temperature of the CMB called the CMB anisotropies. Where a region ended on a stretch the region was cooler and the CMB light is cooler and where it ended on a compression the region was hotter and the CMB light is hotter. These are just tiny effects, a 1 part in 100,000 change in temperature, but they have been measured. Figure 4.2 shows the most detailed map we have of these regions in the CMB taken by the Planck team [52] in 2015. The CMB is a snapshot in time of where each region end up in it's cycle of oscillation.

This is not the only information we can get from these patterns. Figure 4.3 shows the temperature differences in the CMB measured by the Planck team

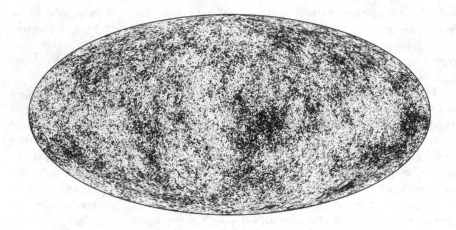

Figure 4.2: Map of the CMB anisotropies across the whole sky. The small fluctuations in temperature are the CMB anisotropies. From the Planck Collaboration, 2016, *Astronomy and Astrophysics*, 594, A1, 38. Credit: ESA and the Planck Collaboration.

[53] in 2013 plotted against the size of the region. The size gets smaller as you go along the horizontal axis (as the angle gets smaller). In this graph the oscillations from the early universe can be seen. The solid line is the theoretical prediction from the ΛCDM model and the points are the measured values. The ΛCDM model fits the measurements extremely well.

To explain these peaks and troughs we need to understand how fast the oscillations were moving. We can see from the graph that the denser regions were of many different sizes. The biggest regions would have pulsated very slowly and the smaller regions very quickly. The speed at which the particles were moving was determined by the properties of the universe at that time. The atomic matter was moving in a soup of matter and light and it moved through this primordial soup in a similar way that sound waves move through air. We hear sound by the particles in the air moving in a wave and hitting our eardrums. By analogy, we call the speed that waves in the primordial soup moved as the speed of sound.

The speed of sound of the primordial soup was about half the speed of light. From this speed, we can calculate the size that the biggest regions would have been to make only one compression in the time the universe was 1 second old up to 380,000 years old. We call this the 'sound horizon' – the maximum distance matter could have travelled in 380,000 years. This is the first peak in the CMB anisotropies. It shows where gravity had pulled the particles inwards in a single compression and it corresponds to the largest regions. We calculate that these regions today should be 490 million light-years across and, this is the amazing part, this is the value that is measured from the CMB anisotropies.

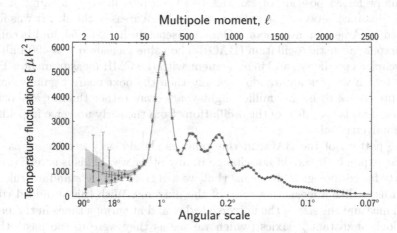

Figure 4.3: Power spectrum of the CMB anisotropies. Graph of temperature difference plotted against the angular size of the fluctuations. The
baryonic acoustic oscillations can be seen in the peaks of the graph. From
reference by Planck Collaboration, 2014, "Planck 2013 results. XV. CMB
power spectra and likelihood", *Astronomy and Astrophysics*, 575, A15,
60. Credit: ESA and the Planck Collaboration.

The second peak in the CMB anisotropies are at a size where the regions
have had time to compress and expand once, these regions are half the size of
the first peak. The third peak is the regions that have compressed, expanded
and compressed again, they are a third of the size; and so on. The smaller
regions would have made many compression and expansion cycles. In the
Planck CMB anisotropy graph we can measure up to 15 peaks. From the first
three peaks we can calculate the amount of matter in the universe, how much
of that is dark matter, and the shape of the universe. These measurements
give us an accurate picture of the universe.

Let's now come back to how we see the oscillations in the positions of
galaxies in the universe today. The freezing in of the oscillations gave a preference for where galaxies ended up. This preferred position was caused by the
same thing that caused the first peak of the oscillations that we see in the
CMB. The largest regions only made one compression and so they had the
most time for matter to build up at the edges of the regions. These edges
would be at the same radius from the region's centre because they were determined by the speed of sound of the primordial soup. The edges have grown as
the universe expanded and the extra matter means that they will have extra
stars and galaxies in them. This gives a slight preference for where galaxies
exist today; some preferring to be at the centre of the regions and some at
the edges. We expect this distance between the centre and edges to match the
CMB distance of 490 million light-years.

This preferred position of galaxies has been measured by looking at the average distance between two galaxies across large areas of the sky. It was first detected by American astronomer Daniel Eisenstein in 2005 [54] and is called the baryonic acoustic oscillation (BAO). The value measured was 490 million light-years, as predicted, and in agreement with the CMB measurements. This means that if we pick any random galaxy then the next nearest galaxy has a slight preference to be 490 million light-years away rather than at any other distance. This is the effect of the oscillations from the early universe imprinted on the universe today.

The pattern of the BAOs in the galaxies should only get bigger as the universe expands, it should not change in any other way. This is a very useful property for cosmologists. It means that we can treat it as a 'standard ruler' – we can use it like a measuring ruler of the universe. With this standard ruler we can measure the size of the universe today and at various times in the past. If we look at distant galaxies (which we see as they were in the past) then we can see how much smaller the BAO length was in the past by measuring the average distance between these galaxies. By doing these measurements for increasingly distant galaxies we can determine how much the universe has expanded at different times in it's life. This could confirm the acceleration of the expansion due to dark energy and it could give us another way to measure the Hubble constant, perhaps with more accuracy. As our measurements of distant galaxies improve then we expect our knowledge of dark energy and expansion to improve. The discovery of the BAO standard ruler in galaxies was important evidence that contributed to the acceptance of ΛCDM as the Standard Model of Cosmology.

Having one of these measurements of the primordial oscillations is great, having both is wonderful, and the fact that they agree is fantastic. They are Cosmological Clues and provide evidence for the ΛCDM model of structure formation in the universe. As Valérie de Lapparent said [41] when she mapped the cosmic web "The galaxies appear to be on the surfaces of bubble-like structures". The ΛCDM model tells us that the bubbles formed from pulsating particles when the universe was 380,000 years old.

4.2.3 The Cosmological Parameters

The Standard Model of Cosmology can be defined by ten numbers that are called the cosmological parameters. They are the set of quantities whose values are not predicted by ΛCDM so we have to measure them to know what values to put into the model. Some of them are the initial conditions for the universe, the values we need to put in the model to define the early universe, and some of them are values that we need to put in the model to define what the universe looks like today. There are many combinations of parameter values that are consistent with the laws of physics, each one defining a different universe, but we want to find the set of values that defines our particular universe and for that we need to measure them.

It is possible to get a set of consistent parameter values by using only data from the CMB. The *Planck* team analysed several years of data from the *Planck* satellite and produced what are today's benchmark cosmological parameters [55]. The 2018 parameters are the latest and most accurate set to date and combine measurements from the CMB temperature, the CMB anisotropies and CMB gravitational lensing. To constrain the set even further, the CMB data is combined with data from BAO measurements. The result is a set of ten parameters that, when put into the ΛCDM model, they provide a description of the universe that fits much of the evidence.

What are these ten numbers? We have seen most of them before although they may be presented in a way that is unfamiliar. The most familiar one is the Hubble constant (H_0) with a value of 68 km/s/Mpc (this means that for each 1 mega-parsec (3.3 million light-years) of space, it is expanding by 68 kilometres every second). The age of the universe (t_0) is 13.79 billion years old which is known to an accuracy of 20 million years.

Then there are the relative amounts of the different components in the energy density budget: dark energy (Ω_Λ), dark matter (Ω_{DM}) and atomic matter (Ω_b). Figure 4.4 shows these relative amounts in a piechart. Most of the universe is made up of dark matter and dark energy, stuff that we don't know what it is, and only a small amount (less than 5%) is the stuff surrounding us on Earth.

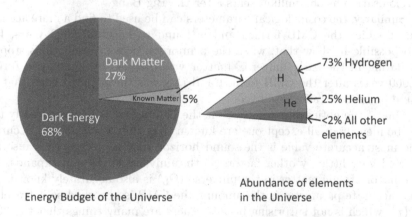

Energy Budget of the Universe

Abundance of elements in the Universe

Figure 4.4: The energy density budget of the universe. The known (atomic) matter makes up less than 5% of all the energy in the universe and most of the universe consists of dark energy. Also shown is the abundance (by mass) of the chemical elements in the universe. Almost all of the known matter in the universe is hydrogen and helium.

The parameter Ω_0 tells us whether the universe is flat or curved. The data fits well to a flat universe, giving a value of one for Ω_0. A flat universe means that adding up the values of all the energy densities, Ω_b, Ω_{DM} and Ω_Λ, gives a total of one. A flat universe has no overall curvature of spacetime. For cosmologists that simplifies our calculations so we are not complaining, but it is a little strange that it is exactly flat (see Section 5.9 on Flatness Problem).

The last four numbers are a little more complicated. Three of them relate to the primordial density fluctuations discussed in the previous section (the denser regions that formed in the early universe). These are the initial conditions of the universe. We need to know how many and how big the density fluctuations were and that information is captured in the parameters A_s and n_s, the amplitude and slope of the primordial power spectrum (for a discussion on these parameters see Section 5.5). The other initial value is the distance of the sound horizon which is quoted as an angle, Θ_{MC}, with a value of one degree corresponding to a distance of 480 million light-years. These initial parameters determine how matter grew into stars and galaxies and what the cosmic web looks like today.

The last parameter is to do with how much the CMB light is absorbed on route to us today. This is the parameter τ with a value of 0.05. When the first stars formed, their light stripped electrons from atoms in the reionisation process. The freed electrons then scattered the CMB light as it travelled to us today. By knowing the value of τ it is possible to calculate when the first stars formed and reionisation happened. The *Planck* CMB data gives an age of reionisation as 657 million years after the Big Bang.

Similarly, the cosmological parameters can be used to find a more accurate age at which the CMB formed and is found to be at 372,000 years. It is also possible to show that, when the primordial density oscillations stopped oscillating in the early universe, matter was dragged by light for a further 18,000 years after the CMB formed and this was the point in time that the sound horizon distance was fixed.

One of the noticeable things about the parameters is how accurately they can be measured; all except one are known to within a few percent accuracy. The most accurate value is the sound horizon distance (Θ_{MC}) because it is affected very little by other factors as the universe grows and expands. The amount of atomic matter in the universe (Ω_b) is also accurately known. The least accurate parameter is the amount the CMB is absorbed as it travels to us (τ), which is not surprising because there are many things that the CMB light can, and does, encounter on it's journey to us.

Observations from galaxies support the CMB values of the cosmological parameters with a few discrepancies. The parameter where there is the biggest difference is in the value for the Hubble constant. This is called the Hubble tension (discussed further in Section 6.5). There is also a small difference in the dark energy parameter between the CMB and supernova measurements. This may be due to our lack of understanding the details of supernova evolution and the difference is enough to search for what could be causing it.

ΛCDM is a model of how the universe expanded and cooled, how matter and it's structure formed in it, and it is held together by a set of cosmological parameters that fit together to give a consistent picture. It brings together the six Cosmological Clues and puts specific, well measured values to the model. It is a powerful model and is accepted as the working cosmological theory.

4.3   THE STEADY STATE UNIVERSE

The Steady State Theory is a universe that does not change with time, it has always looked the same in the past and will always look the same in the future. It has expanded forever and will continue to expand forever. The theory struggles to fit the evidence from the Cosmological Clues and most scientists have abandoned it although there are still some astronomers who work on ideas for an unchanging universe. So why are we discussing it?

The Standard Model of Cosmology is well established now, but it hasn't always been like that. In the 1940s scientists were working on developing a theory that could explain an expanding universe given the evidence at the time. The Big Bang model was struggling. It had measured the age of the universe as 2 billion years and the age of the Earth was known to be at least 4.5 billion years from radioactive dating. So other theories were being explored. The main alternative to the Big Bang was, and still is, the Steady State Theory. The competition between the two theories, Big Bang and Steady State, provided the impetus to gather more evidence which eventually led to the Big Bang being generally accepted. The Steady State Theory was important historically and understanding it also helps us to gain insight into other possible ways to look at the universe. In addition, it is always good to know what has been tried and rejected in order to avoid repeating the same work and sometimes in science rejected ideas can come back into favour again.

The idea started with three British friends, Herman Bondi, Thomas Gold and Fred Hoyle who worked together on UK naval research into radars during the Second World War. The story goes that the three astronomers had watched a horror film together. The film ended with the same scenes as it began. This got them thinking about whether the universe could be in a continuous loop. They went on to publish their ideas in 1948 but not together; Bondi and Gold [56] published the idea starting from one viewpoint and Hoyle [33] published it from a different perspective. This set up a scientific rivalry between them that possibly affected the development of the theory.

Bondi and Gold were looking for a theory that would allow the universe to be unchanging in time. They based their theory on the concept of a 'perfect cosmological principle' which they defined as the universe being uniform and "stationary in its large-scale appearance as well as in its physical laws". Keeping the laws of physics the same throughout all of space and all of time was an important aim for them. From the assumption of this principle they argued that the universe must expand and that matter must be continuously created in space in order to replace the matter that was expanding away. This kept the density of matter in the universe always the same. It was proposed that hydrogen atoms are created (a proton and an electron) and that one hydrogen atom would be produced in each cubic metre of space every 300,000 years. The rate of production was based on matching it to the average density that the universe is today. (For comparison there are 10 trillion trillion atoms in the same volume in air.) This rate of production is so small that we will not be able to see it happen. Over time, the new hydrogen atoms form clouds of gas which eventually join together to form stars and galaxies.

Fred Hoyle was motivated by the Big Bang model, he wanted to show that it was wrong. He was one of those scientists that challenges the current thinking, comes up with imaginative ideas, and was not afraid to argue for them. (He also wrote many books including science fiction.) As we saw in Chapter 2, this is an important role in science even if the ideas turn out to be wrong. Hoyle was successfully working on nuclear reactions in stars and developed the Steady State theory in order to show that all chemical elements could be created in the universe without the need for a Big Bang.

Hoyle argued the Steady State Theory from a mathematical perspective, asking the question, can the cosmological equations produce a universe that is always the same? He used Einstein's theory of relatively and added an extra term that he called his 'creation field' (the C-field). This is similar to how the cosmological constant (dark energy) is added into these equations, but the creation field creates matter and the cosmological constant expands space. The resulting equations continuously create matter in the universe and from this the perfect cosmological principle follows. Although the outcome of the two papers was similar, the subtle difference between how they were argued caused a rift between the friends.

The Steady State Theory was not the first proposal for matter to be continuously created in the universe. As far back as 1928, the British physicist, astronomer and mathematician, James Jeans, proposed an idea where "matter is poured into our universe from some other, entirely extraneous spatial dimension" [57]. Needless to say that at the time this was thought to be a bit of a wild idea but today talking about other spatial dimensions is part of our mainstream science.

The Steady State can be considered as a good theory in the sense that it makes a very definite prediction that can be tested. If the universe is unchanging then the age, type and density of galaxies that exist today should be exactly the same as in the past. When we look at light from distant galaxies it has taken a long time to reach us so we are seeing it from the past – the further away the galaxy the further back in time we are seeing. The universe has kindly provided us with a time machine so we can test this theory.

This is where the theory starts to fall down. When observations of distant galaxies were made this was not what was seen. Across the road from where Hoyle was working in Cambridge, Martin Ryle was using radio telescopes to look at distant galaxies. His work on radio astronomy won him a Nobel prize in 1974, the first one awarded for astronomy. What Ryle found was that radio galaxies were brighter in the past. This was the opposite of what Hoyle wanted to find and he had heated debates with Ryle. There was a possibility that only the brightest galaxies are seen at far distances, so the debate continued.

Then the Cosmic Microwave Background (CMB) was discovered in 1964. This was easily explained by the Big Bang, but was difficult to explain using the Steady State Theory. Hoyle proposed that the CMB was light scattered by galactic dust. For this to be the case the CMB would have characteristics in it that come from the dust that the light scattered from. This is not what is seen in the CMB, it is extremely uniform. When the pure blackbody curve of it's temperature was seen in 1981 that clinched the argument. The CMB could not be from scattered light. The Steady State theory could not explain the evidence and was rejected by most scientists.

Hoyle was undeterred. In 1966 he developed new versions of the Steady State theory along with Indian astrophysicist, Jayant Narlikar [58]. Previously, it was proposed that the matter was created in space, now the matter was created where there was already large amounts of matter, such as in galaxies, and the newly created matter moved into space. A second development was the 'Hoyle-Narlikar bubble universe' [59]. The universe consists of many bubble universes each one with matter creation happening within them. Some bubbles stop creating matter and expand. As they expand the matter from surrounding bubble universes pours in. This could produce a universe that continually expands and contracts. At the same time, Hoyle was also continuing his calculations on the amount of helium in the universe to counter the Big Bang and developed ideas on supermassive objects acting as mini oscillating universes.

In the 1990s Hoyle tried again, working with Narlikar, Halton Arp, Chandra Wickramasinghe and Geoffrey Burbidge [60] they put the previous modifications together into a unified theory. The result was called the Quasi-Steady State Cosmological model (QSSC). In this model matter is created during little big bangs called 'mini-bangs', that are smaller than the Big Bang and they don't start from a singularity. These mini-bangs happen about every 15 billion years (about the age of the universe as calculated by the Big Bang model) and appear throughout all of space and time. The universe has no beginning and the creation of matter causes the expansion of the universe. QSSC calculates the observed abundances of the elements and explains the amount of matter in the universe using just the elements (atomic matter) so there is no need for dark matter in the model.

That leaves the problem of explaining the CMB. The Steady State Theory says that the CMB light is scattered light from stars. To make the CMB very uniform there had to something special to scatter the light, galactic dust would not do that. What Hoyle added to the QSSC model was microscopic metallic 'whiskers' made from iron and graphite that float around in space. These would scatter the starlight in a particular way to make the CMB very uniform. The density of these whiskers would be extremely low so they are unlikely to be seen. Although they have not really been looked for, to date no metallic whiskers have been found.

When dark energy was found in 1998 the QSSC was modified again to fit the observations. Hoyle was convinced that the QSSC model could explain the Cosmological Clues without breaking any laws of physics. In a review in 2000 [61] Hoyle described dark matter and inflation as 'add-ons' to the Big Bang and called them 'epicycles' in reference to the Ptolemy geocentric universe 2,000 years ago.

A good scientific theory predicts the evidence. An issue with the Steady State Theory was that the theory kept changing to fit the evidence after it had been observed and any predictions, such as galaxies being the same in the past as today, have been shown to be wrong. Hoyle did not give up though and even up to his death in 2001 Hoyle refused to accept that the universe could start with a Bang. Today there are only a handful of scientists working on the Steady State Theory and it continues to be a lone voice alternative to the Big Bang model.

4.4   COSMIC INFLATION

Cosmic inflation takes us back to the early universe before the Standard Model of Cosmology begins. It is a theory that provides answers to two of the Cosmological Problems that ΛCDM cannot answer. It is not part of the Standard Model of Cosmology and you will see why later. So what is cosmic inflation? It is when the very early universe expanded extremely rapidly and then stopped, creating all the matter in the universe and leaving the universe gently expanding as we see it today. You could say that inflation was the birth of the universe.

Cosmic inflation was proposed by American physicist, Alan Guth, in 1981 [62], in order to solve the Horizon and Flatness Problems that arise out of ΛCDM. From measurements of the Cosmic Microwave Background we can see that the universe is at the same uniform temperature everywhere. This should not be the case, in the ΛCDM model there are parts of space that have never have been in contact with each other so they should be at different temperatures. This is the Horizon Problem. The Flatness Problem is that our cosmological evidence tells us that the universe is flat rather than any other shape. This is a very specific, unique shape and there is no reason why the universe should be exactly flat. These problems are discussed further in Chapter 5.

In the very, very early universe, before the ΛCDM model starts, the universe was very small. The region that became our whole universe could have been smaller than the size of a proton. Inflation says it then rapidly expanded (approximately to the size of a football). For inflation to work the expansion has to be at an exponential rate, that means it continually doubles it's size, and it does this about 100 times (2^{100}). This gives an increase in size equivalent to a microscopic bacteria expanding to bigger than the Milky Way. It was more expansion than has occurred in the 13.8 billion years since inflation finished. The time it took to expand this amount was tiny, just 10^{-35} seconds. This was an extraordinarily fast rate of expansion, much faster than the speed of light. How can this be, nothing can go faster than light according to the theory of relativity? In this case, it is space itself that is expanding faster than light so it is allowed.

So what started the rapid expansion?

Guth had an answer to what caused inflation to happen. In physics we have the concept of an energy field, these come from quantum theory of particle physics. An energy field is where each point in space has an amount of energy associated with it, for example a magnetic field is an energy field. The more energy the field has the stronger it is. The field strength determines the forces on particles and other fields (for example, magnetic fields can move iron particles). Energy fields always reduce their strength to be the lowest energy they can be, which in the early universe was determined by the temperature. The lowest point an energy field can reach is called the vacuum state. The field will still have energy but it cannot reduce it's energy any further. That is why we talk about the vacuum state of the universe having energy. Guth proposed that there is an energy field associated with inflation and he called it the 'Inflaton Field'. As the temperature of the universe started to cool the inflaton field lowered it's energy. It then reached an energy where it could not go any lower. The interesting thing that Guth did was to say that the inflaton field did not go to the very lowest it could be but got stuck at an intermediate energy. This is called a false vacuum state. In this false vacuum state the inflaton field had a lot of energy.

As the universe cooled further the inflaton field couldn't reduce it's energy because it was stuck in the false vacuum, so it started to exert a force on space itself, pushing it outwards and expanding it very rapidly. The inflaton field became a constant field strength in a cooling universe. As the universe expanded the field strength stayed the same and expanded it some more but now there was more space so it expanded even more, causing an exponential expansion. We have seen a constant field in cosmology already, it is the cosmological constant that is dark energy. Dark energy's constant strength has the effect of expanding space. The difference is that dark energy has a very weak field strength and we see it's effect because it is in a vast amount of space. The inflaton field had a very strong field strength within a very small volume of space. In this false vacuum state the inflaton field was constant and expanded the universe but, unlike dark energy, it did it very rapidly because it was a very strong field.

We have now seen how inflation started and how quickly it expanded space but it also needs to stop otherwise there would not be a universe today that we live in, it would still be exponentially expanding and any particles would be so far apart there would be no gravitational interaction so no stars. So what caused inflation to stop? Guth proposed a mechanism for this.

The rapid expansion of space also rapidly cooled the universe until it was almost empty and it reached a point where the temperature of the field was significantly lower than it's strength. This supercooled the inflaton field. An example of supercooling is seen in water which can be a liquid below 0°C if the ice crystals are prevented from forming.

Inflation and supercooling would have continued forever unless the inflaton field could get out of the false vacuum state and get into the lowest energy possible of the true vacuum state. This is where quantum theory comes in. Within the inflaton field there were quantum fluctuations. Somewhere in space there would have been a fluctuation in the energy that took the inflaton field out of the false vacuum state and into the true vacuum state. This created a bubble of space where the inflaton field reduced to the lowest vacuum state and stopped inflating. The bubble had undergone what is called a phase transition, it had changed from the inflating phase (supercooled) to the non-inflating phase (not supercooled). The phase transition change happened rapidly. The bubble grew (close to the speed of light) and dragged the surrounding regions into the same state, which did the same and very rapidly the whole universe was in the true vacuum state. (Each bubble is called a nucleation point, similar to bubbles in boiling water). By this time, there was no more exponential inflation and the universe was left uniformly expanding at whatever speed it was when inflation stopped. This is the standard expansion that we see today (called Hubble expansion). The processes of supercooling and phase transitioning out of the supercooled state were essential for inflation to stop.

This is not the end of the story though. There was another very important thing that the inflaton field did as it stopped inflation. It created matter. As the bubbles stopped inflation, the energy of the inflaton field reduced to match the energy of the true vacuum state. This energy had to go somewhere and it went into making particles. It made inflaton particles (a hypothetical and unseen particle) which are unstable and they decayed into more stable particles which are the ones that exist in the universe today. These newly created particles were extremely hot so that the universe was also at a very hot temperature. Now instead of a cold empty universe there was a hot universe full of hot particles. The universe had been reheated. So all the matter that is in the universe today was made in the very short time it took for the bubbles to stop the universe inflating. The process of reheating was an essential process for the universe to change from an empty cold (supercooled) universe to one that contained matter and heat. The temperature and conditions of the universe became what we expect it to be after the Big Bang and not long after (about a second) the ΛCDM model begins.

The matter that was created by the inflaton field was all created in the same conditions so it is all at the same temperature. This is what is seen in the temperature of the Cosmic Microwave Background. Our measurements show that the CMB is very uniform and the same everywhere and inflation predicts this. The Horizon Problem was solved. What about the Flatness Problem? When the universe was very small it could have any shape. As it expanded the shape was also expanded. It expanded so much that we see only a small part of it and it will always look flat (just as the Earth looks flat to us even though it is a large sphere). This solved the Flatness Problem.

Inflation is a wonderful idea. It is based on known physics, it has a mathematical framework, and it pulls together many ideas into a consistent and elegant theory. It tells us why the universe is expanding today, how matter was formed and it also solves the cosmological problems of horizon and flatness. As Guth himself said [63] "With inflation, however, we have a theory of the bang itself – the outward thrust of the big bang can be attributed to the repulsive gravity of the false vacuum".

There is a problem with it though, one that Guth in his original paper had identified. Inflation happened too quickly. When the bubbles formed the energy in them was released at their boundaries forming 'firewalls' of hot particles. This would have produced a universe of vastly varying temperature, the very problem that Guth was trying to solve. One solution to this is to have lots of bubbles that collided and spread their energy so that then maybe the universe would be at a more uniform temperature. The problem with this is that if there were too many bubbles then inflation would not have lasted long enough to solve the horizon and flatness problems. This is called the 'graceful exit problem'.

There is a modification to Guth's inflation theory to fix this problem, proposed a year later by Andrei Linde [64] and separately by Andreas Albrecht and Paul Steinhardt [65]. The rate at which the inflaton field reduced to the vacuum state was slowed down so that the bubble nucleation sites did not form and the phase transition happened slowly and uniformly. This meant that there were no firewalls and the temperature of the universe was very uniform as required. This modification is called 'slow-roll inflation'. The combined theory of Guth's inflation with the slow-roll modification is called 'new inflation'.

There is also another problem that inflation solves. This comes from particle physics theories called grand unification theories (GUTs) and they predict that at phase transitions in extremely high temperatures, like that in the very early universe, then heavy magnetic monopole particles should be created. These are particles that have only one pole of a magnet (either a North pole or a South pole). GUTs requires many of these monopoles to be created because any changes took a long time. With inflation the changes were very quick which restricted the number of monopoles created and once created they were rapidly expanded away from each other, so the density of them in the current universe is predicted to be very small. No monopole particles have been seen, but inflation gives us a reason why they have not been seen.

Cosmic inflation not only solves two Cosmological Problems and the monopole problem but it is also a theory that is based on two key foundations of physics, general relativity and quantum mechanics. So why is it not part of the ΛCDM model? For a theory to become part of the Standard Model of Cosmology scientists need to be convinced by the evidence and there is no evidence supporting inflation. Although it predicts the smoothness of the

CMB temperature spectra it does not give us any predictions we can use to test the theory. It also introduces further unanswered questions. What is the inflaton field? What are inflaton particles? What causes the slow-roll? Many scientists include inflation in their day-to-day working model because it fits so well with ΛCDM but it will not become part of the Standard Model until there is more conclusive evidence.

4.5 MODIFIED GRAVITY THEORIES

A fundamental assumption of our models of the universe is that the laws of physics are obeyed. When Newton developed his law of gravity he based it on how he saw gravity behave on the Earth and in the Solar System. The law works very well when we consider things the size of the Earth and the Solar System. They don't work well for places where there is very high gravity such as a black hole. In these places we need to use Einstein's theory of relativity. This is not just an add-on to Newton's law but a whole new way of looking at gravity, it is a paradigm shift in scientific thinking. Newton said that gravity is a force. Einstein said that gravity is not a force, instead it is space curving and bending around masses (Earth, galaxies, black holes) and then other objects moving within this curved space. The way two objects move through curved space is what appears as gravity. So we already have two ways of looking at gravity that work on different scales, the Newtonian force of gravity that works on Earth and places of average gravity, and Einstein's relativistic curved space that we use in places of very high gravity (although general relativity works for all strengths of gravity).

When dark matter was proposed it was not a popular idea, how could the universe be made of mostly stuff that we know nothing about. As an alternative to dark matter some scientists looked at the possibility of changing how gravity works in galaxies. This meant changing the laws of gravity that we rely on for all our other science, so also not that popular an idea, but a few scientists worked on it. These ideas were not very fruitful until the 1980s.

Mordehai Milgrom, an Israeli physicist, was looking at the mathematics of how galaxies rotate. Measurements of rotation curves of galaxies had found that they did not behave as they should when Newton's law of gravity was applied. They were flat when they should have been going curved (a flat rotation curve is shown in Figure 3.5). The standard way of explaining these flat rotation curves was by introducing dark matter. Milgrom wanted a different explanation. He thought that maybe the laws of gravity worked differently in regions of very low gravity, such as in the outer edges of a galaxy where matter is less dense. When he looked at the rotation curves he noticed that he could make a simple change to Newton's law that would make the galaxies rotate in the way that was being observed. What he did was change the acceleration due to gravity. Instead of the force of gravity being related to the acceleration (a) as Newton had said, Milgrom said that it was related to the square of the acceleration (a^2). When he put this into the equations he found that the rotation curves matched what was observed. His modifications explained the evidence so well that it is now called Milgrom's Law. He published his idea in 1983 [66]. Milgrom calculated the way galaxies moved (their dynamics) by changing Newton's laws of gravity, so the theory is called 'Modified Newtonian Dynamics', or MOND.

MOND not only explains the rotation curves without the need for dark matter. It does more. From the equations it can be shown that the mass of a galaxy is related to it's velocity of rotation (v) to the power of four (v^4). This relationship had already been observed in spiral galaxies in 1977 by Brent Tully and Richard Fisher [6] and is called the Tully-Fisher relation. It is an important way to measure distance to galaxies and forms part of the distance ladder (see Figure 3.2). This relationship cannot be predicted using dark matter, instead a distribution of dark matter has to be picked to fit the observations. On the other hand, MOND predicts the exact Tully-Fisher relation from the mathematics. This is a major achievement for the model.

Newton's law of gravity must still be correct at accelerations that we see in our Solar System, after-all that's what we observe, so there must be a cross-over from Newton's law to Milgrom's law. This is called the boundary acceleration and Milgrom showed that it has a simple relationship to the cosmological constant Λ (dark energy). This was unexpected and cannot be explained. Physicists like these type of coincidences because they may give us a clue to the fundamental workings of the universe, such as a possible link between dark matter and dark energy. What this clue might be we don't know, but there may be one in there somewhere.

MOND has some successes but it is not a complete model of the universe. It cannot explain how galaxy clusters form (although progress has been made on this), it cannot explain the formation of matter in the early universe, and it cannot explain the peaks in the CMB spectra. For these things we still need dark matter. One conclusive piece of evidence for dark matter that MOND also cannot explain is from the observations of the Bullet Cluster (see Figure 3.7). In the Bullet Cluster the visible matter is separated from where most of the mass lies. This can easily be explained using dark matter, the dark matter sits where most of the mass is, but it cannot be explained by MOND. So today, MOND theories include dark matter in them. They do not need as much dark matter as in ΛCDM but still some dark matter is needed.

MOND is limited in what it can do, it only works as a variation to Newton's force of gravity. What we would like is to have a modified gravity theory that works at all scales, from the very small to the very large. For this we need a more general theory based on Einstein's relativity. The hope is that if such a model could be produced then it would explain what is happening in galaxy clusters and the early universe as well and become a viable alternative to ΛCDM. It turns out that there are possible modified relativity theories that can do this but so far they do not match any observations. These theories are simply called 'modified gravity'. Turning MOND into a relativistic theory is not easy. Relativity does not have the concept of acceleration of gravity because gravity comes from the curvature of space. So a very different approach to Milgrom's is needed.

There are many different theories for modified gravity. These theories are very mathematical and work on adding or varying terms in the equations of general relativity which is complicated enough already. We have seen this before when Hoyle added his creation field and dark energy added the cosmological constant. Each modified gravity theory adds or varies different terms which gives the theory a different name, often named after the person who developed it: Brans-Dicke gravity was developed in 1961 by Carl Brans and Robert Dicke [67]. Today, most of the work on these theories try to find alternative ways to explain dark matter, dark energy or inflation.

The leading theory for relativistic modified gravity was developed 20 years after Milgrom's papers by Jacob Bekenstein in 2004 [68] and is called TeVeS which stands for Tensor-Vector-Scalar. The problem with TeVeS is that it is too flexible, it is easy to change many of the parameters to match the evidence, this also makes it very difficult for it to make any predictions. Although this does mean that it can be varied to match structure formation and almost match the CMB, it also means that it is not a very useful theory.

Another variation of modified gravity are theories that produce extra dimensions in space. When we look around us we define the position of an object by three directions, these are the three dimensions of space. Mathematical theories can have more than three dimensions of space. 'Lovelock gravity', developed in 1971 by David Lovelock [69], can have more than four dimensions. A more recent theory called 'DGP' (developed by Gia Dvali, Gregory Gabadadze and Massimo Porrati in 2000 [70]) has two gravities at the same time, one with three space dimensions that dominates at small distances and one with four space dimensions that dominates at large distances and they live in a five-dimensional space. 'Galileons' are a more general version of the DGP theory and can work in even higher multi-dimensional space.

None of the modified gravity theories have evidence to support them. Following the detection of gravitational waves in 2016 [71] it was possible to make accurate tests of general relativity. All the tests have shown Einstein's equations to be accurate. These results rule out many of the modified gravity theories.

In the end, MOND did not achieve what it set out to do which was to remove the need for dark matter. The modified gravity theories today need to include some dark matter and, although it is less than needed in the ΛCDM model, it is still there. What MOND can do is explain how galaxies move better than ΛCDM: on a scale the size of galaxies it works better. The modified gravity scientists say that models of the early universe and galaxy clusters need to be developed that is consistent with the galaxy dynamics. The ΛCDM scientists say that galaxies have more complex processes that we are still finding out about. What we can take away from this is that there are alternative theories that work for just bits of the universe and that ΛCDM does not work for everything in the universe. Although there is no evidence for the relativistic models of modified gravity, the more limited Newtonian MOND model does fit galaxy evidence very well and it also helps us to understand the limitations of the ΛCDM model.

4.6   MULTIVERSES AND OTHER UNIVERSES

4.6.1   Of Strings and ToEs

There are many non-standard theories about how the universe could have formed; they are often very imaginative and highly mathematical. Some revolve around the idea that there is a 'Theory of Everything', a ToE. The most well developed ToE is string theory, the idea that particles are made up of tiny, wriggling strings of energy. ToE theories aim to combine the four fundamental forces into one unified theory: gravity, the electromagnetic force (that creates electricity and magnetism), the weak nuclear force (that causes radioactivity), and the strong nuclear force (that holds the nuclei of atoms together). Such a theory could have profound implications for our understanding of the universe but it has eluded scientists for over 100 years, so getting a ToE would be a truly amazing achievement. There are also GUT theories (grand unification theories) that aim to combine three of the four fundamental forces (excluding gravity). There are less ambitious theories, but equally important, that are looking to combine the large scale of gravity with the microscopic scale of the quantum particle world, these ideas are called 'quantum gravity'. They are investigating the possibility of making gravity behave in chunks, we call that being quantised. One possibility is that there is a gravity particle. We even have a name for it, a graviton. We have never seen a graviton, but if we ever did then that could confirm some of our theories of quantum gravity and could be revolutionary. From these ideas we also get the concept of multiverses; that there is not just one universe but many that exist and can even interact with each other.

Our theories of how matter behaves at the microscopic quantum level are well establish and fit the evidence extremely well. We also have the theory of relativity that fits how matter behaves on a large scale. These two theories are not compatible, mathematically and conceptually they are quite different. We would like to have one theory that explained the very small and the very large and everything in between. This is a ToE, a Theory of Everything. String theory is the main ToE that we have today.

Not long after Einstein came up with the idea that gravity is the effect of space being curved, German physicist, Theodor Kaluza [72], started to wonder whether the electromagnetic force could also be described by curved space. He developed the mathematics but he needed to add another curved dimension for electromagnetism to exist in. Amazingly, the equations worked and he had a theory where gravity and electromagnetism could exist in a four-dimensional curved space. What could this other dimension be? Swedish physicist, Oskar Klein [73], came up with a proposal; the other dimension is curled up on an extremely small scale so we cannot see it. These ideas and equations became known as the Kaluza-Klein Theory.

By the 1990s, the Kaluza-Klein theory had been developed into a theory that combined all four fundamental forces into one theory, called string theory. String theory says that all particles, even the smallest sub-atomic particles, are made up of tiny vibrating strings of energy. These strings can vibrate in different patterns to create the different particles that we can detect. There are only certain resonant vibrations that are allowed that are determined by the shape that the strings can form (similar to vibrations of musical instruments being determined by their shape and size). These vibrations are quantised energy. One of the successes of string theory is that it creates a universal force that acts on all particles that looks much like gravity and it does that by using quantised energy. It can explain gravity and all the particles and forces in the universe. It seemed to be the Theory of Everything that is being searched for.

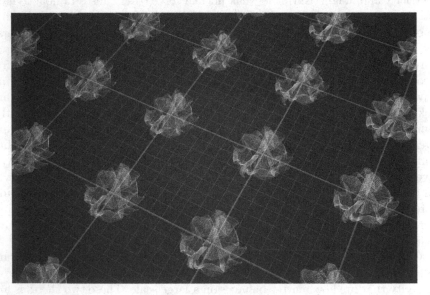

Figure 4.5: An artists interpretation of a multi-dimensional space. The six small dimensions are curled up into Calabi-Yau space which sit on the three large-scale dimensions of space that is familiar to us, represented by the grid structure in the diagram. Credit: Shutterstock.

There are a few problems with the theory. Similar to Kaluza, in order for the mathematics to create extra forces then extra dimensions are needed. String theory requires six extra dimensions of space that are tiny curled up dimensions that we cannot see. There is a mathematical six-dimensional shape called a Calabi–Yau space that could possibly be the shape of these extra dimensions (see Figure 4.5). The vibrations of the Calabi-Yau space could be creating all the particles and forces that we see in our three-dimensional world. A string theory called M-Theory adds another large space dimension so it has ten space dimensions and the one time dimension which all theories have making it an 11-dimensional theory. Unfortunately, we have never seen any evidence for these extra dimensions.

For string theory to work it also needs something else. It needs to add in supersymmetry to become what is called superstring theory. Supersymmetry is where each fundamental particle has a symmetrical partner particle. This is not that helpful because no such particles have been detected but the maths works. To explain why none have been seen maybe these particles are very heavy, meaning that we need very high energies in particle accelerators to be able to see them. Even the energy produced in the Large Hadron Collider at CERN is not high enough which could be why we haven't seen them. The problem with making the partner particles heavy is that supersymmetry is now broken. In addition, supersymmetry creates additional interactions between particles that are known not to exist. To get round this problem another symmetry was added called R-parity.

Another major problem with string theory is that it requires a universe that has a negative cosmological constant. This is the same cosmological constant that we know as dark energy. From our measurements of the universe we know that the value of the cosmological constant is positive.

String theory remains the main ToE in physics. It can be used to describe many different universes but it cannot be used to predict how our unique universe works. Despite being a promising and well developed theory, there is no evidence for string theory and increasing amounts of effort are now being put into other ideas.

Some theories are not trying to provide a solution to everything in physics. Quantum gravity is a class of theories that are looking to make gravity quantised but not looking to unify all the forces. It is hoped that these quantum gravity theories could help improve our cosmological models, for example, to explain what caused the fluctuations that seed matter formation in the early universe or what happens in a black hole. One of the main quantum gravity theories is called 'Loop Quantum Gravity'.

In loop quantum gravity, space is made up of a network of extremely small loops (similar to the small extra dimensions of string theory). Curved space gives us gravity so now gravity can be defined by quanta of curved, looped space. The loops represent the volume of space and links between the loops represent the surfaces where the volumes meet. The mathematics combines general relativity and quantum theory into one theory, but it does not provide us with a solution where we can get back to how gravity works in our universe. Like string theory it is a very mathematical solution and so far loop quantum gravity has solved some problems but also created others.

Producing a theory where gravity is quantised is proving to be difficult. To get round this problem there is another class of theory called 'emergent gravity'. These use the concept that gravity is an emergent property. What do I mean by this? Gravity could be created by the effect of a collection of objects behaving in a coordinated way. An example of this is a crowd in a football stadium producing a wave that goes round the stadium by individuals standing up at different times. One person on their own can't produce the wave, it is an emergent property of many people moving. Gravity could be the same thing. If this is the case then we don't need to know what the properties of the individual objects are so we don't need to quantise gravity. Whether this, or any of the other unifying theories, will gain any evidence for them is something we are waiting for.

4.6.2 Multiverses

The idea that our universe may not be the only universe in existence is called 'multiverses'. A universe that is at the limit of what we will ever be able to see, called the observable universe, could be said to define other universes. The spacetime continuum surrounding our observable universe could be considered as another universe, or other universes, that live next to each other.

There are other more interesting ways that multiverses have been proposed. One of these is related to inflation. An idea developed by Paul Steinhardt, Alexander Vilenkin and Andrei Linde [74, 75] says that during inflation not all regions of space expanded together, some regions stopped inflating resulting in bubble universes each possibly having a different set of laws of physics and fundamental constants. Our universe would be a bubble living within a sea of bubble universes. This multiverse idea is called 'eternal inflation'. There are many quantum fluctuations that could have happened during inflation producing many different bubbles with each one producing more bubble universes, going on eternally. Maybe the bubble universes could have been created by multiple big bangs in the universe, after-all why should our Big Bang have been the only one to happen.

Another way of producing multiverses is using string theory. It can predict many different types of universes each one having different values for the fundamental constants. This is one of the problems with string theory, it can create too many different universes and is not able to predict just one. By coupling string theory to the eternal inflation idea it is possible to produce many different, very strange universes that exist alongside our universe.

Another version of multiverses from string theory comes from 'branes' (by Paul Steinhardt and Neil Turok [76]). Branes are structures from string theory that form in higher dimensional space (more than three dimensions). Our universe exists on a three-dimensional brane floating in four (or more) dimensional space. Other three dimensional branes exist with other universes on them and they float around in the multi-dimensional space. When they collide there is a big bang and the universes reset themselves producing universes that could evolve and expand like our own.

An alternative idea for multiverses is that black holes could produce new universes. A black hole is where matter has become so dense and the gravity so strong that not even light can escape from it. Lee Smolin [77] proposed that microscopic quantum effects in a black hole could lead to it exploding resulting in a big bang and this would start a new universe. Each new universe would have slightly different fundamental constants depending on the small variations of the quantum fluctuations at the time of the explosion and so would behave in very different ways.

The last multiverse idea that I will mention comes from quantum mechanics. This is called the many-worlds interpretation of quantum theory. This is to do with how, on a microscopic quantum scale, matter changes when we measure it. We do not understand the process that causes the change, but we do know that the mathematics we use describes it very well. One interpretation of this measurement problem is that when a measurement is made then all possible outcomes of that measurement come into existence but we only see one of those outcomes, the rest are in many different worlds.

4.6.3 The Holographic Universe

Can the universe really be a hologram? Well there is a theory that says that it could act like one. This may sound strange, almost fanciful, but there are reasons for it which are backed up mathematically. The idea is called the 'holographic principle' and was proposed by Dutch physicist and Nobel prize winner Gerard 't Hooft [78] and put within a framework of string theory by American physicist Leonard Susskind [79].

The idea came from work on black holes. There is a problem with theories of black holes that is called the 'black hole information paradox'. As the black hole swallows up matter, then the information that was contained in the matter is lost. This information is called entropy and one of the fundamental laws of physics, the second law of thermodynamics, states that entropy should always increase (or at least stay the same). A black hole appears to be removing entropy from the universe. This is a problem. Jacob Bekenstein in 1981 [80] proposed that the information from matter falling into a black hole is contained within fluctuations at the surface of the hole.

The holographic principle states that we can know what happens inside a volume of space by encoding it on the surface at the same resolution. What does this mean? It means that whatever we can know about a volume of space we can also know by looking at the surface of the same piece of space. Consider it as information flowing through a surface and we can see only what is at that surface, but from that information we can tell what particles are in there, their temperature, how fast they are moving and all that defines what is inside. Recently, a possible test of the holographic principle was proposed by Erik Verlinde and Kathryn Zurek [81] using gravitational waves. The effect has yet to be detected.

I include the holographic principle because it is one of the few ideas that links gravity, thermodynamics and entropy. Although, so far there is no evidence, I can't help but wonder whether somewhere in the idea is a fundamental concept to do with surfaces and gravity and entropy that could help us understand reality.

The ideas that I have outlined in this section are some of the ideas that are around in physics. The thing to remember about them is that they are ideas. They may have a lot of complicated maths supporting them but the observational evidence is not there. So why do scientists still work on them? In the 1980s, some of the ideas did show promise, string theory was one of them, and the hope was that they could be developed into the full theory of everything. Since then that promise has waned. As the ideas haven't agreed with how our universe behaves then more elaborate and complex ideas have been added to make them fit. Despite much work and many scientists working on these ideas it is still the case that there is no evidence. We should remember though that these are the many ideas that happen before a scientific revolution. So maybe one of these ideas will break through, or maybe something totally different will be found. We wait and see. What we do know is that we do not have a complete theory of the universe yet. There are a couple of upsides to having many new ideas. They do make good science fiction and many films and novels have used multiverses in them. More importantly, they have also captured the public's imagination and maybe they bring people into science that wouldn't have otherwise.

CHAPTER 5

The Problems

What does the ΛCDM model not explain?
The Scientific Process: DISCUSSION

5.1   WHAT IS A COSMOLOGICAL PROBLEM?

The Standard Model of Cosmology does a good job of explaining the Cosmological Clues but it doesn't explain everything and it still has some fundamental problems that have not yet been answered. This chapter discusses eight important problems and their possible solutions. The three obvious problems are what is the Big Bang, what is dark matter and what is dark energy. We may never know what caused the Big Bang, and any solution may be speculative, but we hope that we can find answers to what is dark matter and dark energy. A fourth problem comes from the cosmic web. We have a good theory as to how the cosmic web formed but it relies on there being small fluctuations in the early universe that grew into the large-scale structure of matter that we see today. What caused these fluctuations? Without them the theory of structure formation falls down but we don't know where they came from. This is the Cosmic Web Problem. The fifth problem comes from not seeing all the atomic matter that the model predicts, although this may have been solved.

The three remaining problems are from evidence that cannot be explained within ΛCDM. The Cosmological Clues tell us that the universe is very uniform and looks the same in all places, we see this in the CMB temperature and when we look at the cosmic web on a large scale. The ΛCDM model does not give us a uniform universe, it gives us a universe that should have differences on a large scale. So there is a problem. This is called the Horizon Problem. From our measurements of the cosmological parameters we can determine the shape of the universe. This tell us that the universe is flat. This may seem obvious but it is not. The universe could have been any shape so why is it flat? This is the Flatness Problem.

The final problem comes from particle physics but is still relevant to the Standard Model of Cosmology. In the very early universe when particles were forming the antimatter particles were also forming. The matter and antimatter particles would have been forming and colliding and annihilating in pairs. Today, almost all of the universe is matter so at some point in the past there must have been more matter than antimatter. This is good for us because otherwise, had there been the same amount of both, they would have all paired up and annihilated each other and there would be no matter in the universe and we would not be here. The problem is that we don't know why there should have been a difference between the amount of matter and antimatter. Particle physics theory says that it should not happen. This is the Antimatter Problem.

Should we be concerned that there are at least eight problems with the ΛCDM model? No, it is part of the scientific process to have anomalies and work on solving them. The Cosmological Problems are a sign of a developing theory.

5.2 PROBLEM 1: THE BIG BANG PROBLEM

What was the Big Bang?
Also called The Singularity Problem

The ΛCDM model starts with a hot Big Bang but we don't know what the Big Bang could be. This is the Big Bang Problem. In an expanding universe space is getting bigger and that means when we go back in time space was smaller. Going back even further, all of space, time, matter and energy will become just a single point. This point is called a singularity. (The centre of a black hole could, theoretically, contain a singularity). In a singularity the laws of physics break down and we do not know how it can exist. This is called the 'singularity problem'. What is it? How can an infinite amount of energy be held in an infinitely small amount of space? A singularity may transcend our ability to ever know what it is, it may just be a mathematical construct, but there is a possibility that if we have a theory of quantum gravity then we could at least hypothesise what the Big Bang singularity was within the laws of physics.

There is another problem that comes from the Big Bang and that is what existed before it? As the ancient Greek philosopher Parmenides said "Nothing comes from nothing" so how did the universe even start if there was nothing there before it? We can rephrase that question to 'How did a zero-size universe become a finite-size universe?' In 1984, Alexander Vilenkin proposed a way to answer this question in an idea called 'quantum creation' [82]. This assumes that the zero-size universe obeys the laws of quantum theory so that there is a very small probability that, in the geometry of a zero-sized space, a quantum fluctuation will occur that can overcome the energy barrier that exists between a zero-sized universe and a finite-sized one. This can happen by quantum tunnelling through the energy barrier (a known effect that computers rely on). Once the universe has become a finite size then the Big Bang can occur and expansion start. Quantum creation depends on having a theory that links geometry to quantum fluctuations, a theory that we don't have at the moment but is the quantum gravity theory that is being searched for (see Section 4.6.1). If one universe occurred through quantum creation then others could have formed and multiple universes could exist, taking us to the concept of multiverses. If quantum creation is accepted then the Big Bang Problem becomes 'Where do the laws of physics come from? and 'Do they exist independent of space and time?' We keep answering one problem and creating another but this is the process of science.

Once we have a finite-size universe then the next question is 'What made the universe expand?' Was there a Big Bang explosion? This is where inflation theory provides an answer. In the early universe an inflaton field existed that got stuck in a false vacuum state and caused exponential expansion (see Section 4.4). Once inflation stopped, the ΛCDM model takes over, and the evolution of the universe follows the laws of physics. Inflation can be considered as the birth of the universe (the Bang of the Big Bang) but not the conception. It existed before inflation, perhaps just gestating. There is a possibility that gravitational waves formed during inflation and we may be able to detect them. These are being searched for.

Maybe we don't need the Big Bang at all. Maybe space and time have always existed and the Big Bang was a quantum fluctuation that kick started the expansion. The idea of eternal inflation says that space has always been expanding, with bubble universes forming within this eternally inflating space. There are ideas about universes that are cyclic and new ones form from the remains of old ones in a continual cycle; bouncing universes and the CCC universe model by Roger Penrose do not need singularities or big bangs (see Section 7.1).

To answer the Big Bang Problem there are ideas on how a universe could have formed from nothing (quantum creation), what the Big Bang was (inflation), and what existed before the Big Bang (possibly other universes). We may be able to get evidence for inflation but it's possible that we may never be able to prove how the universe was created. If we accept certain bouncing or cyclic models then we don't need the Big Bang at all, but then we would like to have evidence that the universe does bounce or cycle. Even if we cannot prove these ideas, as scientists we would like to at least have an idea that fits with our known laws of physics, so we keep thinking about the Big Bang Problem.

5.3 PROBLEM 2: THE DARK MATTER PROBLEM

What is dark matter?

The Dark Matter Problem is a simple question, what is dark matter? As we look for an answer we meet WIMPs and MACHOs (physicists do have a sense of humour). We have lots of evidence that dark matter is there and from this evidence we know what properties it needs to have. What we don't have are any particles that behave in this way. We have ruled out some of the things it cannot be and we have some ideas of what it could be but these are still quite speculative. We are searching for some evidence to see if any of these ideas could answer the problem or at least to rule them out. So far we have not detected anything that could explain what dark matter is.

So what are the properties of dark matter?

1. The evidence we have for dark matter comes from it's gravitational interactions: rotation of galaxies, gravitational lensing and the Bullet Cluster. The ΛCDM model relies on dark matter having a gravitational pull to form stars, galaxies and the cosmic web. So the one property we know dark matter has is that it has gravitational attraction. This means we are looking for something that has mass.

2. Dark matter is not dark, it is transparent to light; it does not give off light, it does not collide with light, it does not interact with light. This means we cannot see it.

3. Dark matter does not interact with atomic matter. If it did then we would see the effects; galaxies would have dark matter in the same places as atomic matter rather than in extended dark matter halos around the galaxy, and when the sound horizon was created in the early universe it would have been smaller because the speed of sound through the interacting fluid would have been slower.

4. Dark matter does not interact with itself. If dark matter had self-interactions then there would be no dark matter halos surrounding galaxies. A dark matter particle would eject another dark matter particle from the halo and move to a lower energy at smaller radius. This would be repeated and the radius would continue to shrink and the halo would disappear. This is called the 'gravo-thermal catastrophe'. Although, there are some scientists who are investigating whether dark matter could have a small self-interaction.

5. Dark matter has no charge; otherwise it would interact with an electromagnetic field and that would mean that it would interact with other particles. Since nearly all known particles have a charge then dark matter cannot be any of these. The exception to this are neutrinos, which don't have a charge, but these have also been ruled out because they are light and would not have the gravitational properties that are required of dark matter. (A calculation called the Tremaine-Gunn Bound [83] gives a lower limit for the mass of neutrinos if they are to behave as dark matter but neutrinos are heavier than this limit). This gives us another property:

6. Dark matter is not a particle that exists within the Standard Model of particle physics. This means that we need to find a new type of particle that is beyond any physics that our tried and tested models predict.

7. There is one more property of dark matter that is essential to the ΛCDM model and that is dark matter needs to be cold, after all it's in the title of the model – 'Lambda Cold Dark Matter'. By cold, we mean that the dark matter is moving slowly compared to the speed of light (we say that it is non-relativistic).

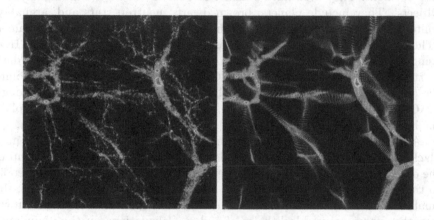

Figure 5.1: Computer simulations of cold dark matter match the observations of the cosmic web. Left: Density map from computer simulations using cold dark matter showing the fine filament structure as seen in galaxy observations. Right: Density map from simulations using warm dark matter showing only the large filament structure and empty voids. Credit: From Figure 3 in A. Schneider, R.E. Smith, A.V. Macci and B. Moore (2012) "Non-linear evolution of cosmological structures in warm dark matter models," *MNRAS*, 424, 684–698.

How do we know dark matter is cold? A good piece of evidence comes from computer simulations. By using a computer to calculate the behaviour of dark matter and atomic matter particles in gravity, from the early universe through to today, we can see galaxies form within a cosmic web. Changing dark matter to be cold, or hot, or warm allows us to test which type of dark matter matches the way the universe looks today. Figure 5.1 shows the results of two different simulations. The left picture shows the cold dark matter simulation which gives the fine structure filaments that are seen in the cosmic web today (see Figure 3.10). The right picture shows warm dark matter which produces the denser, large filaments in the cosmic web but not the finer ones.

Cold dark matter produces structure formation in a hierarchical way; matter forms the cosmic web by small objects collapsing under gravity then growing into larger galaxies and filament structures (bottom-up). Hot dark matter produces the larger structures (clusters) first and then fragments into smaller galaxies (top-down), this makes the core filaments denser with filaments. It is the cold dark matter model of hierarchical structure formation that best fits observations. Some cosmologists are exploring whether there could be a combination of warm and cold dark matter.

What if dark matter is not a new particle but just large lumps of atomic matter that we cannot see such as the remains of dying stars, or stars that are not big enough to have started nuclear fusion? This has been explored. These 'compact' objects do exist and are difficult to detect because they do not give out light. They even have a name: MACHOs – 'MAssive Compact Halo Objects'. They include planets, brown dwarfs, neutron stars and, arguably, white dwarfs, red dwarfs, and black holes. In 2000, the wonderfully named "The MACHO Project" reported on almost 6 years of looking for MACHOs using gravitational lensing [84]. What they found was that maybe 20% of dark matter could be explained by MACHOs, although other groups have found the amount was only 1%. It is generally accepted that there are not enough MACHOs to be the complete picture. In addition, MACHOs do not explain the baryonic acoustic oscillations that are seen in the CMB and galaxies.

A speculative MACHO is the primordial black hole. These are possible mini black holes that formed in the very dense regions in the primordial soup of the early universe. They would have been different sizes, from the microscopic to the massive, and there would have been lots of them. If they formed, the smaller ones may have evaporated away and the larger ones may have grown into the supermassive black holes of today. Calculations on the abundance of primordial black holes show that there were not enough of them to be considered as dark matter. Although primordial black holes were proposed in 1966 [85], the idea fell out of favour but the recent detection of black hole mergers from gravitational waves, and the possibility of now being able to detect small black holes if they exist, has brought the idea back into debate. There is even a speculative suggestion that the elusive Planet 9 could be a primordial black hole.

So if dark matter cannot be something that we know, then maybe it is a new type of particle. What could this new particle be? There are three types of particles that have been seriously investigated: neutrinos, WIMPs and axions.

Neutrinos have been ruled out because they are too light and hot (they have very low mass and move close to the speed of light). There is a possible neutrino candidate called the sterile neutrino. This is an undetected type of neutrino that only interacts through gravity. If they exist then they could be dark matter. It may be possible to see sterile neutrinos through oscillations from the other types of neutrinos that do exist. A recent neutrino detection experiment called MiniBooNe [86] at Fermilab (2018) reported neutrino oscillations that hint that sterile neutrinos may be possible to detect if they exist.

WIMPs are particles that are heavy, cold (slow-moving), and very weakly interacting with matter, hence the name: 'Weakly Interacting Massive Particles'. The main WIMP contender is the neutralino. The neutralino is a hypothetical particle that comes out of supersymmetry theory (called SUSY). We have seen supersymmetry before in the discussion on string theory (see Section 4.6.1). The neutralino is a heavy, stable particle with no charge and weakly interacts with other matter, so it has the required properties of dark matter. None have been detected but it would be exciting if we did find it.

One of the properties of dark matter is that it does not interact with atomic matter, so why are we looking for a particle that weakly interacts with atomic matter? Calculations on the rate dark matter particles and antiparticles would need to annihilate to have the correct amount of dark matter in the universe today show that they can interact at the strength that matches the weak nuclear force. This has been called 'the WIMP miracle' and it could help us find dark matter. Detecting a particle that has no interaction with matter other than gravity is extremely difficult. If dark matter interacts very weakly then we may be able to detect it, so this is what we are looking for. You may consider this to be a long shot, and maybe it is, but in science we can only do the experiments that are possible to do at the time, and there are some experiments that we can do to see if we can find a WIMP. If we find one then we could solve the Dark Matter Problem, and if we don't then we have ruled WIMPs out, which also gives us information.

A third type of particle that could be dark matter is called the axion. An axion is a particle that comes from a new type of field that was proposed by Roberto Peccei and Helen Quinn in 1977 [87]. It does not require SUSY and can be part of the Standard Model of particle physics. An axion has no charge and weakly interacts with light but not matter. It is a light particle so if it is dark matter there would need to be a lot of them. Interestingly, the axion was named after a detergent because if found it would clean up several problems in physics, including the 'strong CP violation problem' and the 'neutron spin problem' from particle physics, as well as solving the Dark Matter Problem (and possibly the Antimatter Problem [88]).

There is an alternative to dark matter being a new type of particle; it could be a new state of matter. Such proposals are called exotic dark matter. Exotic matter is not a solid, liquid or gas but exists in a different state that can behave in strange ways; for example, superfluid liquid helium can climb up walls. Maybe dark matter can be matter in an exotic superfluid state [89, 90], with no viscosity and no interaction with matter in a normal state. Alternatively, dark matter could exist in different states depending on the environment it is in, so in low temperature environments at the edge of a galaxy it could be a superfluid, but in high temperature environments like the early universe and galaxy clusters it could be in a normal fluid state.

In the search for dark matter we have ruled out the matter that we know, MACHOs and neutrinos, and we are now looking for the ones that are new types of matter. These particles are speculative and so far there is no evidence for any of them: WIMPs, axions or sterile neutrinos. There are ideas that dark matter could be a new type of superfluid state of matter or primordial black holes. Maybe dark matter doesn't exist at all; changing how gravity behaves has been shown to explain some of the evidence that requires dark matter. Finding a dark matter particle could confirm some supersymmetry ideas in particle physics and maybe solve some other problems as well. What is generally accepted is that finding dark matter may well uncover some new physics. Of course, the thought of finding new physics is very exciting for physicists so the hunt for dark matter goes on.

5.4 PROBLEM 3: THE DARK ENERGY PROBLEM

What is dark energy?
Also called the Cosmological Constant Problem

Something is causing the universe to accelerate it's rate of expansion and we don't know what it is. This is the Dark Energy Problem. We don't know much about dark energy. We know it pushes space, creating a negative pressure so it expands. Gravity is only attractive and pulls matter together; mass attracts mass, it never repels. Dark energy is only repulsive, it repels space, and in that sense, dark energy can be considered as anti-gravity.

There exists a mathematical way of thinking about dark energy. The equations of general relativity (GR) include a term called the cosmological constant (Λ). This was added into GR by Einstein to make the universe not expand or contract. When Hubble found that the universe was expanding then the cosmological constant was taken out of the GR equations. When dark energy was discovered then the cosmological constant was put back in again to include an acceleration of expansion.

If dark energy is the cosmological constant then it has a property that can explain the acceleration. For dark energy to be constant, then as the universe expands the dark energy has to get stronger, otherwise as space got bigger then the dark energy density would get smaller and there would be no acceleration. What happens is that the more space there is, then the more dark energy there is, so the density of dark energy stays constant. The strength of dark energy is small and in the early universe space was small so there was not much dark energy. As the universe expanded and space got bigger the amount of dark energy has got bigger and now there is a lot of it and we can see the effects in the acceleration. It is only in the last two billion years that the accelerating effect of dark energy has dominated the expansion of the universe.

The weird thing about a constant dark energy density is that energy is being created as space expands. This seems to contradict the law of conservation of energy, a law that physicists do not break. It is allowable though. This law only applies to a static, non-expanding space where Newton's laws apply. In an expanding space, where space is changing with time, the laws of conservation of energy do not apply and energy can be lost and gained. What is conserved though is the energy density.

What is the Cosmological Constant? The answer to this is dark energy but what is dark energy is answered by 'it's the cosmological constant'. So mathematically the cosmological constant is helpful but it doesn't answer what is dark energy. What we want is a physical explanation of what dark energy is.

A possible physical explanation could come from the vacuum energy of space. Space has energy and the lowest energy it can have is called the vacuum state. This is not zero; from quantum theory we know that there are quantum fluctuations in the vacuum state from which particle pairs can form and annihilate, called virtual particles. They live for a very short time between the events of real particles. The vacuum energy is an energy that we know exists within space so maybe it is dark energy. If dark energy is the vacuum state then we can calculate how much energy there is. Knowing how fast the universe is accelerating we can calculate that the vacuum energy density would be 10^{-8} erg/cm^3. We can also calculate the energy density of the vacuum state from quantum theory. From this we get a value of 10^{112} erg/cm^3. That is not just a big difference, that is an unbelievably enormous difference; a difference of 10^{120} times. Either dark energy is not the vacuum state or our understanding of quantum theory is wrong. This is called the 'vacuum catastrophe'.

The quantum energy in the vacuum state is so big that there would not be a gently expanding universe, there would have been so much energy that expansion would have been rapid and no stars or galaxies would have formed. There is a solution to this. The theory of supersymmetry can produce an opposite energy that cancels out the quantum vacuum energy. This sounds great, but it introduces another problem. SUSY cancels out the vacuum energy so that it is zero. To get the tiny value of dark energy from the vacuum energy there would need to be some fine tuning of the value of SUSY to exactly match the dark energy value. This then becomes a 'fine tuning problem' that astronomers do not like. It seems too coincidental and we like to have a reason why a value is what it is. The problem of fine tuning led to ideas of the 'anthropic principle'; that the universe is as it is today because otherwise we would not be here. They then led on to ideas for multiverses based on the premise that all possible values of Λ can exist in other universes but only our value of Λ produced stars, galaxies and life. Many scientists do not like the anthropic principle because it is not falsifiable so do not consider it scientific.

A more scientific explanation could be that the cosmological constant is changing and becoming smaller over time. It has been evolving for so long that it is almost zero and has reached the value that we see for dark energy. This idea is called 'quintessence'. The name comes from the latin term Quinta Essentia meaning Fifth Essence and quintessence is sometimes called the fifth force. This was another scientific problem that Nobel prize winner James Peebles worked on [91].

If dark energy is not the vacuum energy, are there any other alternatives? There are a few ideas such as holographic dark energy, ghost condensates, dark fluid flow and let's not forget matter creation from the Steady State Theory which could create a push on space. These are speculative and require some evidence, but they are interesting ideas.

There has been recent work that suggests that maybe dark energy does not exist. Jacques Colin and team [92], in 2019, looked at 740 supernova and suggested that the dark energy previously observed may be an artefact due to the movement of Earth, although most scientists accept that dark energy exists.

Another theory that avoids the need for dark energy comes from the voids in the cosmic web. If the Milky Way lives within the Local Hole, a very large void in the cosmic web, rather than outside it then the space we live in would have less density than outside the void and there will be negative pressure around us. This could look like dark energy. As more observations are being made about the Local Hole then the evidence in support of this theory is getting less.

Dark energy is a puzzle. We have evidence for it, although there are still some doubters, and it does fit with many aspects of the ΛCDM model but it is hard to explain where it comes from. We are still trying to understand what dark energy is; it could be the cosmological constant or it could turn out to be more complex. We need more data and more Cosmological Clues.

5.5   PROBLEM 4: THE COSMIC WEB PROBLEM

What are the primordial fluctuations that seeded the cosmic web?
Also called the Density Fluctuation Problem

An important strand of the ΛCDM model is how the structure of matter forms: the stars, galaxies and the cosmic web. This is a complex process involving dark matter, oscillations in the early universe, the birth and death of stars, and galaxy mergers, all within an expanding and cooling universe. The model works well. It can explain much of what we see in the sky and we have developed computer simulations that can recreate the cosmic web as we see it today.

There is a missing piece though and that is why did structure formation happen at all? For matter to form into clumps there had to be denser regions for the clumps to start from. If all matter were evenly spread throughout the universe there would be no differences in gravity between different regions so there would be nothing to pull the matter together. So where did these initial denser regions come from? What were the seeds of structure formation?

The seeds of structure must have formed in the very early universe because there is no mechanism within physics that could have caused them after the universe was one second old. The denser regions had to be there before the ΛCDM model starts and they had to be large enough by then to provide enough gravity to pull matter into oscillating clumps. ΛCDM does not explain where they came from; they are assumed to have been there. This is the Cosmic Web Problem.

A possibility is that the denser regions could have been created by quantum fluctuations in the hot early universe. This is an attractive idea, and is within the laws of physics, but ΛCDM does not have enough expansion to turn quantum fluctuations into the size of galaxies today nor into the size of the temperature fluctuations of the CMB by the time the universe was 380,000 years old.

A solution to this is to expand the universe by a very large amount, very rapidly, so that the quantum fluctuations become large enough. This is what inflation does. The quantum fluctuations can happen in the very early universe and are expanded exponentially and rapidly to become big enough to be the seeds of structure in ΛCDM. In a normal, Hubble expanding universe, any quantum fluctuations will be short lived and can disappear (annihilate). In an inflating universe quantum fluctuations form as space is exponentially expanding and a fluctuation will get stretched beyond the point where they annihilate so stay in existence. New fluctuations are created and they are stretched and this continues until inflation stops. Now the universe is full of small density fluctuations of all sizes, from the quantum size of the fluctuations that formed at the end of inflation, to the size of the universe of the fluctuations that formed at the beginning of inflation. It is what we call 'scale invariant' – there are equal numbers of each size. If we took a picture of the early universe on a large scale it will have looked exactly the same as when we zoomed in a thousand times, or a thousand times more; we would not have been able to tell the difference between the pictures. A graph showing the number of fluctuations at each size would be just a flat horizontal line - this graph is called the power spectrum of the density fluctuations.

We can look for this property of the fluctuations using the Cosmic Microwave Background (CMB). The density fluctuations were imprinted on the CMB when the universe was 380,000 years old, these are the 'blobs' that we see in Figure 4.2. We can use the CMB to measure the properties that the density fluctuations have by using the power spectrum of the CMB temperature anisotropies. The measurements show that the fluctuations are almost scale invariant as predicted by inflation. The flatness of the power spectrum graph is measured using the cosmological parameter n_s. An n_s value of one means that the fluctuations are exactly scale-invariant (the graph of number of fluctuations plotted for each size is flat). The *Planck* CMB measurements give a value of 0.958 which is almost one. The small deviation from one is called the 'tilt' of the initial density fluctuation spectrum.

Different models of inflation theory predict different values of n_s. By comparing the predictions from the different inflation theories to the measurements of n_s using the CMB it is possible to determine if one model is better than the others. It may also give us evidence for inflation theory and it is hoped that the next generation CMB telescopes may be able to do this.

There is other evidence from the CMB that can be explained by inflation. There are fluctuations in the CMB that are bigger than 1 degree, the size of the horizon (see the Horizon Problem Section 5.7). In ΛCDM, the Horizon Problem means that there should be no fluctuations larger than 1 degree. Inflation solves the Horizon Problem and allows the fluctuations to be much bigger, as observed.

There are other, more speculative, ways that the universe could have seeded the structure of matter. Cosmic strings are possible large, one-dimensional defects caused by phase transitions as the universe cooled (they are not the same as the microscopic strings in string theory). These were speculated to have formed structure due to their gravitational attraction but it is now thought that they would not give the scale invariant spectrum that is seen in the CMB. Maybe the universe is holographic and the seeds are formed from higher dimensions leaving their imprint on a lower dimensional universe. Maybe we don't need any seeds of matter. If the universe did not have a beginning but is cyclic or bouncing then the structure of the old universe could leave imprints that form the structure of the new universe.

There are various ideas as to what caused the seeds of the structure of matter but inflation is the best and preferred theory to solve the Cosmic Web Problem. For inflation to be accepted as the solution then some evidence is required. Perhaps the power spectrum of the density fluctuations could provide this evidence. If inflation did happen, then we exist due to microscopic random fluctuations that were a consequence of the quantum behaviour of the universe. Without these quantum fluctuations then matter would not have gravitated together and we would not be here.

5.6 PROBLEM 5: THE MISSING BARYON PROBLEM

Where is all the atomic matter?

One of the outcomes of the ΛCDM model is that the amount of atomic matter, the matter we know and can see, is only 15% of all the matter in the universe. The rest is dark matter. When we add up all the atomic matter in the stars of galaxies it comes to only 10% of the total atomic matter required by ΛCDM. If we add the gas and dust that we can see then that takes it to about 50% of the total. So where is the rest of the atomic matter? This is the Missing Baryon Problem.

Why is it called the Missing Baryon Problem? In cosmology, atomic matter is known as baryonic matter. Baryons are the protons and neutrons that make up the nuclei of atoms. To make an atom, electrons are combined with the nucleus. Electrons are a type of particle called a lepton and are tiny compared to the baryons. A proton has 1,836 times more mass than an electron so when we are considering the mass of an atom it is mostly coming from the baryons.

As we are capable of seeing more detail and look further out into the universe, we are seeing more objects that have low brightness, such as brown dwarf stars, that are difficult to detect. These can account for some of the missing baryons but nowhere near enough. The most likely place for them to exist is in the filaments of the cosmic web. If most of the baryons are in the filaments then why can't we see them? The hypothesis is that the baryons in the filaments are at a temperature that means that they do not emit or absorb light so we cannot detect them.

Hot gas, the gas that exists in galaxy clusters, consists of charged particles that emit X-rays. Cold gas is at a temperature where the electrons can combine with the hydrogen nuclei to form neutral hydrogen atoms which absorb light. Both the emitted X-rays from hot gas, and the absorbed light in cold gas, can be detected. If the baryons in the filaments are hot enough then at the electrons can leave the hydrogen atoms to form a gas of charged particles, but cold enough that they cannot emit X-rays, then we will not be able to see them. This is warm-hot gas and is at a temperature of between 100,000 and a million degrees. This warm-hot gas sits between the galaxy clusters and is called 'warm-hot intergalactic medium' or WHIM.

There are several ways that WHIM has been detected. The first is similar to how the abundance of helium and deuterium is measured using primordial gas clouds (see Section 3.5). A bright quasar is found that sits behind a filament and is used as a light source. As the quasar light passes through the filament gas there are specific wavelengths of light that are absorbed and can be detected. For WHIM we are looking for the evidence of charged oxygen gas since that has absorption at the temperatures of the WHIM. This technique was used by Taotao Fang [93] in 2010 by looking at quasar H2356-309 through the Sculptor wall of the cosmic web with two different telescopes. The result showed evidence that the missing baryons could be living in the filaments.

In 2020, Macquart and team [94] used five fast radio bursts (FRB) as the light source behind the filaments. FRBs are very short, intense bursts of radio waves from a galaxy. To see one you have to be lucky enough to be looking in the right direction as it hits Earth and it is only with very recent telescopes that it has been possible to know which galaxy it came from. Their result provides evidence that all the missing baryonic matter can be accounted for in the filaments.

In 2019, two independent teams used the Sunyaev-Zel'dovich effect (SZ) to look for WHIM. As the CMB light passes through hot gas it hits high energy electrons and gets an energy boost. This is the SZ effect and it makes the CMB temperature map slightly hotter in the regions where there is the hot gas. The temperature difference is very small but can be detected by looking for it between pairs of galaxies that exist in filaments. Many galaxy pairs have to be added up to make a detectable signal. Hideki Tanimura and team [95] added up 240,000 pairs of galaxies, and Anna de Graff and team [96] a million pairs, to find the tiny SZ signal. The results also show that the baryons in the filament WHIM could be enough to account for the missing baryons.

Further work to improve and confirm these measurements is ongoing but it may be that the Missing Baryon Problem is no longer a problem. This is a relief to cosmologists because if the missing baryons could not be found it would bring into question the validity of the Standard Model of Cosmology. This is one Cosmological Problem that may be solved.

5.7 PROBLEM 6: THE HORIZON PROBLEM

Why is the universe so uniform?

A foundation stone of the ΛCDM model is the cosmological principle. This states that there is no special place in the universe, it should look the same wherever you are. All locations should have the same laws of physics and the same fundamental constants that apply to them. On a large scale (bigger than galaxy clusters) this is true, the universe does look the same. The problem is that the ΛCDM model does not predict a uniform universe. It is a fundamental problem for ΛCDM.

Let's start with what is meant by a uniform universe. There are two ways the universe must look the same. It must give the same observational evidence at all locations; this is homogeneity. It must also look the same in all directions; this is isotropy. These are not the same. A brick wall is an homogeneous pattern but it is not isotropic. If you look at a brick wall upwards you will see a square pattern, if you look at it sideways you will see a rectangular pattern, and if you look between the two you will see a different pattern again. It looks different in different directions; it is not isotropic. If you now move to a different part of the wall the pattern is the same, it still looks different in different directions, but in exactly the same way as before; it is homogeneous. We can also get patterns that are isotropic but not homogeneous. A spherical galaxy would be an example of this. From the centre of the galaxy it looks the same in all directions, but the centre looks different than the edges where there are less stars. The cosmological principle requires the universe to be both homogeneous and isotropic, to look the same in all places and in all directions. It does this but only on very large scales. Even on the scale of galaxies the universe is not the same, we've just seen that a galaxy looks different in different places, and of course galaxies are distributed unevenly across the universe.

The Cosmological Clues give us evidence that the universe is uniform. The CMB gives us the best evidence for this from the extreme uniformity of it's temperature across the whole of the sky (see Figure 3.8). The cosmic web gives us a further clue showing that the distribution of matter across the universe looks the same in all directions when it is looked at in chunks that are 300 million light-years across. This is direct evidence of the cosmological principle. Although we need to be a little careful with this statement. When we look at the uniformity of the CMB light we are testing isotropy, the universe looks the same in all directions. In practice, we cannot test homogeneity because we cannot move to a different place in the universe to see if it is the same but, from what we can see, we assume that it is. Not all scientists think that we should use the cosmological principle, for example, Karl Popper was unhappy with making the assumption of uniformity into a principle, he said "I dislike making of our lack of knowledge a principle of knowing something"[97].

Maybe the universe is not quite as uniform as we think. Recent work by K. Migkas and team [98] in 2020 looked at X-ray light from the gas in galaxy clusters. They calculated the cluster brightness from the temperature of the gas and, by comparing the brightness to what we see on Earth, they could measure the Hubble constant. What they found from analysing hundreds of clusters is that the Hubble constant varies depending on the direction of the cluster. This result needs confirmation but if it is true then it questions whether the universe is isotropic.

We will now look at why it is called the Horizon Problem. Since the universe is a finite age, and no object can travel faster than light, then what we are able to see is limited by how far light can travel since the universe began. This means that we will only ever be able to see a portion of the universe. The furthest distance that we could theoretically be able to see is called the 'observable universe'. The edge of this observable universe is the horizon. The size of the observable universe has a radius of 46.5 billion light-years around us (a diameter of 93 billion light-years). Any light from objects beyond this horizon will never have been able to reach us either in the past or today (see Figure 5.2).

You may think that the observable universe should be a distance of 13.8 billion light-years because light has been travelling at the speed of light throughout time so that is how far light has travelled given the age of the universe. Firstly, the horizon diameter is twice this distance (27.6) because 13.8 is the radius of the horizon from us (the horizon is a big circle around us). Secondly, if we calculated the observable universe without any expansion then this would be true (we call this the co-moving distance). If we include expansion then we see much further. Hubble showed us, from our first Cosmological Clue, that the further away an object is the faster it moves away from us. There will be a distance where space is expanding at the speed of light and at this point light will appear to have stopped. This is called the 'Hubble horizon'. Space outside of the Hubble horizon is expanding faster than the speed of light so the light from a galaxy outside will be moving away from us.

But wait! How can anything go faster than light? Einstein's theory of relativity says that nothing can move within space faster than the speed of light. What we are talking about is space itself moving faster than light and that is allowed in relativity.

The Hubble horizon is not the observable universe though, we can see further. The expansion of space is also making the Hubble horizon expand, and as it gets larger at faster than the speed of light it can overtake the light coming towards us from an object beyond the Hubble horizon and now the light will be able to reach us because it is inside the Hubble horizon. The distance that is the furthest an object can be for us to still be able to see it is called the 'particle horizon'. The particle horizon is the limit that light could

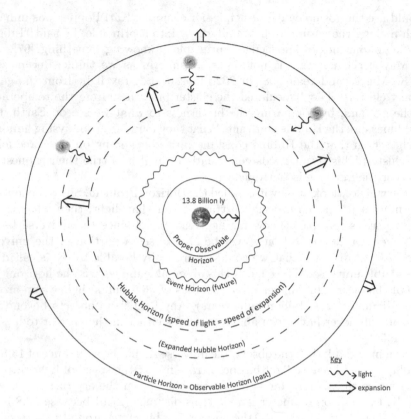

Figure 5.2: Different horizons from Earth. The particle horizon is the observable universe. The Hubble horizon is where expansion of space is at the speed of light. The event horizon is the furthest distance we will be able see an event that happens today (we will see it in the future). The proper (co-moving) observable horizon is the observable distance calculated if expansion is not included. Credit: C. Devereux and P. Farrell.

have reached us by today from events in the past; it is the observable horizon of 93 billion light-years.

There is one more horizon and that is the 'event horizon'. If a galaxy at the particle horizon emitted light today, we would not be able to see it in the future because the universe is continuing to expand (and accelerate due to dark energy). The furthest distance we could see an object in the future that emits light today is called the event horizon and is 16 billion light-years.

We now get to the Horizon Problem itself. If we look at two regions of the sky that are 180 degrees apart (say North and South) we see exactly the same CMB temperature. For two regions to be the same temperature they need to have come into contact at some moment so that particle collisions could even out the temperature differences between them.

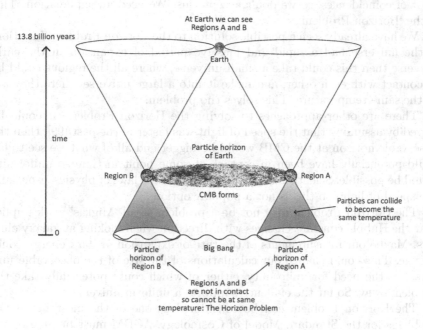

Figure 5.3: The Horizon Problem. Credit: C. Devereux and P. Farrell.

We are seeing the light from the CMB at the moment it was formed and that is when the temperature was determined. For the North and South regions to be at the same temperature they must have been in contact for at least some time before the CMB was formed. The problem is that, between the Big Bang and the CMB forming (380,000 years), there was not enough time for those two regions to have been in contact. If we take our current observable universe (93 billion light-years) and extrapolate back to when the CMB was formed then we can see 85 million light-years across. This is the distance our North and South regions would have been apart but this was not the observable horizon when the CMB was formed. The universe was expanding and the observable horizon was not much bigger than about 1.4 million light years. The North and South regions at 85 million light-years across could never have been in contact, light could not have travelled that far in 380,000 years (see Figure 5.3).

If we treat the sky as the surface of an imaginary sphere around the Earth and divide it into regions that could not have been in contact at the time of the CMB, then there are over 40,000 regions where their observable horizons were not big enough to meet. Yet, they are all at exactly the same temperature. From the laws of physics this should not happen. Maybe it happened by coincidence, but scientists don't like coincidences, and 40,000 coincidences is a lot of coincidences, so we don't accept this. We need an explanation. This is the 'Horizon Problem'.

We have already seen a possible solution to the Horizon Problem. Inflation. If the universe had a rapid and massive period of expansion in the early universe then this could take a small universe, where all the regions could be in contact with each other, and make it into a large universe where they are at the same temperature. This solves the problem.

There are other approaches to solving the Horizon Problem. It could be solved by assuming that the speed of light was faster in the past [99], then the observable horizon at the CMB would be bigger and all of what we see today could potentially have been in contact at some point in time so uniformity would be possible. Scientists don't like to change the laws of physics, especially the speed of light, so this is not a popular option.

The Horizon Problem may not be a problem at all. Migkas' work implies that the Hubble constant changes with direction when looking at galaxy clusters. Maybe our measurements of the rate of expansion or dark energy could change. This could change our calculations of the size of the observable universe, or the need for uniformity, either of which could potentially take the problem away. So far the evidence supports a uniform universe.

The Horizon Problem can be considered as one of the most important problems for the Standard Model of Cosmology. ΛCDM must be able to tell us why the universe looks uniform, after all the cosmological principle is a key foundation of the model and our Cosmological Clues confirm uniformity with evidence from the CMB and the cosmic web. Fortunately, there is an answer to the problem provided by inflation theory. If we can get evidence that inflation happened then we can accept it as part of ΛCDM and the Horizon Problem will be solved, until then it remains a Cosmological Problem.

5.8 PROBLEM 7: THE FLATNESS PROBLEM

Why is the universe flat?

The universe is flat. Not flat like a disc because that is a two-dimensional surface but the shape of spacetime itself for the whole universe is flat. This may not seem surprising but it is. We know that spacetime can be curved. From the theory of relativity, Einstein told us that gravity comes from the curvature of space, so curved space exists all over the universe wherever there is any object, big or small. Figure 5.4 shows the Sun curving space around it, causing the Earth to move within the curved space and orbit the Sun. This is gravity. The smaller curvature of space due to the Earth can also be seen in the figure. So if space is curving all over the universe what is the total amount of curvature in the universe? This turns out to be zero. This is what we mean by flat. Why is there no curvature of the universe as a whole? The universe could have any curvature and being flat is just one, very specific, value. So why is the universe flat? This is the Flatness Problem.

Figure 5.4: Curved spacetime. The Sun and Earth warp spacetime, represented by the grid, and then move within the warped spacetime. Gravity is the curvature of spacetime. Credit: T. Pyle/Caltech/MIT/LIGO Lab.

As cosmologists, it is particularly important that we know the shape of the universe because it affects our calculations of the cosmological parameters and it will determine what will happen to the universe in the future, that is something we would like to know.

There are three types of curvature that the universe can have: positive, negative or zero. Figure 5.5 shows what this means in two dimensions. Zero curvature is a flat plane, like a piece of paper. A positive curvature is a shape like a sphere. A negative curvature is a shape like a saddle. The geometry of three-dimensional volumes behaves in a similar way to two-dimensional surfaces so we will stick with the two-dimensional analogy because it is much easier to understand (and to draw). In a flat space parallel lines stay parallel and a triangle will have angles that add up to 180 degrees. This is the geometry that we get taught at school. When we go to a shape with positive curvature then parallel lines do not stay parallel but will meet (like the longitudinal lines of Earth meeting at the North pole) and a triangle's angles will add up to more than 180 degrees. For the universe, a positive curvature would mean that when we look at further and further distances we would eventually see the same galaxies again and again as we loop round the curved space (just like going round the World and ending up back at home). Space in a positively curved universe would be closed and the universe could end by collapsing back in on itself. In negative curved space the opposite happens and parallel lines get further apart, a triangle's angles add up to less than 180 degrees and the universe is an open shape and will expand forever.

Using the CMB, and these properties of triangles, we can measure the curvature of the universe. The temperature map of the CMB (see Figure 4.2)

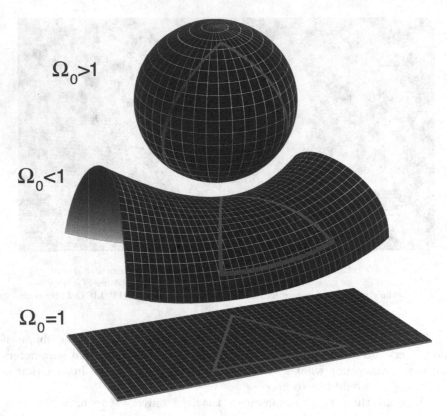

$\Omega_0 > 1$

$\Omega_0 < 1$

$\Omega_0 = 1$

Figure 5.5: Three possible curvatures of spacetime in two dimensions: a sphere (positive curvature), a saddle (negative curvature) and flat (zero curvature). The shape of a triangle is shown on each surface. Credit: NASA/WMAP Science Team.

shows the tiny temperature fluctuations (the anisotropies) that we measure. In section 4.2.2 we saw that these fluctuations were formed from the oscillations of matter in the early universe and are determined by the distance of the sound horizon. We know what this distance should be and we also know when the CMB formed. So we can make a triangle with one side being either end of a 'blob' on the CMB anisotropy map (formed from the oscillations) and the other two sides the distance they were from us when they formed. If the universe is flat then the smallest angle in the triangle should be 1 degree. If it is positively curved it will be larger and if it is negative it will be smaller. What we measure is that it is exactly 1 degree to an accuracy of 0.2%.

This may not seem very flat but the real problem comes when we extrapolate back to the early universe. The expansion of the universe over time will have exaggerated any curvature. So to get a flat universe to a 0.2% accuracy today then at the beginning of the universe it had to be flat to one part in 10^{60}. This is like changing the Sun's mass by adding a couple of particles. To get space to be flat to this accuracy cannot be a coincidence but the ΛCDM model does not have an explanation for it. This is why the Flatness Problem is a problem.

Once again inflation theory comes to the rescue. It solves the Flatness Problem by having a period of massive expansion in the very early universe. Any curvature the universe had before inflation will be enormously expanded. Our observable universe today is just a small part of the total universe so that we are seeing just a small patch of curvature in a bigger curved space. This patch will look flat because it has been stretched so much. This is similar to the way we see the Earth as flat because we are seeing a small patch of a very large sphere.

It may be that the universe is not as flat as we think. Recent work by Eleanor di Valentino and team [100] in 2020 reanalysed the CMB data. They looked at all the 'blobs' on the CMB map, not just the ones at the sound horizon, and they looked at the gravitational lensing of the CMB light. What they found was that there was more matter in the universe than previously measured. The extra matter is enough to give the universe a positive curvature. It is not very curved, so probably not enough to close the universe (expansion and acceleration means it won't collapse), and beyond a certain distance expansion will be greater than the speed of light so there will be no lapping of the universe and we won't be seeing the same galaxy multiple times.

As our measurements of matter density, expansion, and dark energy improve then there is always the possibility that the Flatness Problem may go away but with the evidence we have today the universe looks very flat; flat enough to cause a problem for the ΛCDM model. Of course the Flatness Problem could be solved by using a different model of the universe than ΛCDM but we don't have one that solves it at the moment. Our best solution today is to add inflation to ΛCDM and for this to happen we need new Cosmological Clues for inflation.

5.9   PROBLEM 8: THE ANTIMATTER PROBLEM

Where did the antimatter go?
Also called The Baryogenesis Problem

The universe is made of matter. This seems an obvious statement but from our known laws of physics there should be no matter. In the early universe matter was created. When matter is created, it is always created in pairs of matter and antimatter and very quickly it is destroyed in pairs of matter and antimatter. So if the same amount of matter and antimatter was produced and then destroyed why is there any matter in the universe? This is the Antimatter Problem. For any matter to exist in the universe there must have been fractionally more matter than antimatter. So where did that little bit of antimatter go? Or put another way, why was there more matter than antimatter in the early universe?

We have the Big Bang Nucleosynthesis theory that predicts the hydrogen and helium abundance in the universe. We would like a similar theory that explains how much atomic matter formed and why it is 5% of the total energy budget. Such a theory is called 'baryogenesis' but we do not have one. It is the hope that if we can find out why matter and antimatter were different in the early universe then maybe that will provide a prediction for the exact amount of matter in the universe today and the baryogenesis problem will be solved.

How much difference does there need to be between matter and antimatter? A rough estimate for this is based on how much light and how much matter we see in the universe. For each matter particle in the universe today there are one billion light particles (light comes in packets which we call photons and can be considered as particles). When matter annihilates with antimatter it produces light. We estimate that for each one billion matter particles that annihilated then only one matter particle survived. This gives us a difference of one billion plus one particles of matter to each one billion antimatter particles. A very small, but very important difference. It is this difference that allows there to be any matter in the universe today.

The idea of antimatter has been around since the 1880s but the modern concept of antimatter was predicted by Paul Dirac in 1928 [101]. Dirac was working on combining relativity with quantum theory for the electron and he found an elegant mathematical solution but there were extra terms that looked like the opposite particle of the electron. These turned out to be the antimatter of electrons - the positron. Positrons were discovered four years later by Carl D. Anderson [102] when looking at cosmic rays and received the Nobel prize in 1936 for this discovery. Every known particle has an antimatter particle; they are identical in their mass and in every way except they have the opposite charge and spin. Antimatter annihilates rapidly with matter so they are only seen from the interactions with other particles such as in high energy particle accelerators or from cosmic rays.

The starting assumption in physics is that the laws of nature are the same for anti-matter as for matter. This seems a good place to start but if it was true then there would be no matter. So there must be at least some small difference in the way matter and antimatter behave. We call this an asymmetry; the behaviour between matter and antimatter is not symmetrical. There are three types of symmetry that could be broken by antimatter:

- **Charge symmetry**. Change the charge of the particle (for example from positive to negative). This is called charge conjugation, C.

- **Mirror symmetry**. Reflect the particle in a mirror. This is called parity inversion, P.

- **Time symmetry**. Reverse the time by reversing the motions and the spins. This is called time reversal, T.

We can combine these actions; a CP symmetry changes the particle's charge and reflects it in a mirror. If CPT is applied to a matter particle it becomes it's own antimatter particle.

In 1967, Andrei Sakharov [103] formulated three conditions that are necessary for matter to exist today:

- **Condition 1.** Conservation of baryon number must be violated; otherwise there will always be the same number of baryons as anti-baryons. (A baryon (a proton or neutron) is assigned a number of +1 and the antimatter baryon of −1).

- **Condition 2.** The C and CP symmetry must be violated; otherwise interactions will produce the same number of matter and antimatter particles.

- **Condition 3.** There must be temperature differences (non-thermal equilibrium); if the interactions take place at the same temperature then there will be as many matter-to-antimatter interactions as antimatter-to-matter.

The third condition is met in the early universe as it is cooling down and rapidly changing temperature.

The second condition requires C symmetry violation and, although theoretically it could be possible, is has not been observed. There have been observations of CP violations. The discovery that the neutral kaon particle shows CP violation [104] won James Cronin and Val Fitch the Nobel prize in 1980. More recently in 2019 [105], evidence was found at CERN for CP violation in the charm quark particle.

The first condition requires that the total baryon number must be the same before and after any interaction. If the baryon number of the universe at the Big Bang is assumed to be zero then conservation means that it has to stay zero and there will be as much antimatter as matter, so for there to be a difference then conservation of baryon number must be violated. There is a mechanism for this in particle physics discovered by Gerard 't Hooft in 1976 [106]. By adding small corrections to quantum theory, an effect called the Spharelon can destroy the conservation of baryon number; antimatter baryons can turn into leptons (electron type particles) and baryons can turn into antimatter leptons. Spharelons are hypothetical and there is no evidence that they exist and there is no evidence for condition 1. In addition, the calculations show that they would not be strong enough to create the numbers of observed baryons.

So it is theoretically possible to meet the three Sakharov Conditions. The problem is that the effects are too small to be able to explain the amount of baryons that there are in the universe today. So maybe a different condition is needed.

A possible extra condition is to say that CPT symmetry needs to be violated. This may produce a strong enough effect to create the quantity of baryons observed. The ALPHA experiment at CERN is testing CPT symmetry by creating antimatter hydrogen and comparing it's properties with normal matter hydrogen (NASA estimated that a gram of anti-hydrogen would cost $62 trillion to make).

The evidence rules out the known interactions of the Standard Model of particle physics to solve the Antimatter Problem so another approach is needed. Perhaps it could be solved by a new hypothetical particle such as the inflaton that comes out of inflation theory or the axion that is proposed as a dark matter particle. We will have to wait for any evidence of these to be able to know whether they do. Alternatively, a new theory for the unification of the forces (GUTs) or quantum gravity may provide an answer but a suitable model does not exist yet. All the above discussion is based on the amount of matter and anti-matter being created equally just after the Big Bang and then particle interactions changing the proportions. Of course an alternative theory is that they were created unequally, but we do not have any ideas as to why that would happen within the laws of physics.

We know the conditions that are needed to solve the Antimatter Problem, and there are known particle interactions that do meet these conditions, but they cannot explain the quantity of baryons that exist today. There are other ideas for new particles that could explain the asymmetry between matter and antimatter but there is no evidence for these. So the Antimatter Problem remains an unsolved problem.

We have seen that the ΛCDM model does not explain all the evidence we have: the flatness, the uniformity and the lack of antimatter. We have also seen that it introduces new concepts that we cannot explain; dark matter, dark energy, the Big Bang, and primordial fluctuations. This is why ΛCDM is a model and not a theory, there are still anomalies that need to be solved. Inflation theory can explain three of the problems and if inflation is verified then the Horizon Problem, the Flatness Problem, and the Cosmic Web Problem could be solved. The Big Bang Problem may never be solved but we may be able to develop hypotheses consistent with the laws of physics. We continue to hunt for dark matter and explore dark energy. Maybe if we find an axion it could solve the Dark Matter Problem and the Antimatter Problem. Solving these Cosmological Problems may require new technology, or new physics or adding something else to the ΛCDM model. Solving these problems is what makes science exciting.

CHAPTER 6

The Testing

What new Cosmological Clues are we looking for?
The Scientific Process: FUTURE WORK

6.1   WHERE WILL NEW CLUES COME FROM?

Traditionally, the clues for an astronomer have come from the sky, looking through telescopes with our eyes and surveying the stars and galaxies. Technology now allows us to do surveys where we do not use our eyes at all. Specialised equipment allows us to measure the light from the sky at all wavelengths (a wavelength is the distance between two peaks of the light wave), from X-rays to radio waves, each wavelength of light telling us something different about the universe (Section 6.1.1). Telescopes in space contain complex detectors and technology beaming images and information back to Earth, and some of the new ground-based telescopes don't look like telescopes at all, they cover multiple countries and require supercomputers to get an image.

We can survey the sky for light from objects such as stars and galaxies (Section 6.7), for background light such as the Cosmic Microwave Background (CMB), for cosmic particles such as cosmic rays and neutrinos, and for gravitational waves that are the ripples of spacetime itself. The combination of these different ways of seeing and measuring the universe is called 'multi-messenger astronomy'.

Gravitational waves were first confirmed in 2016 when the ripples of space from the merging of two black holes was detected. This has created a whole new way of surveying the universe. Potentially, it can be used to see beyond the CMB into what the universe looked like in the early fog of baryonic acoustic oscillations (BAOs) and possibly before that. Some ideas say that we may be able to detect the gravitational waves of the Big Bang itself. Gravitational wave astronomy is in it's infancy as a technique and could revolutionise astronomy.

Today, the work of an astronomer is much more than surveying the skies.

Computers provide a way for cosmologists to do experiments by creating artificial universes allowing us to test out different models and theories (Section 6.1.2). The hunt for dark matter (Section 6.3) takes us into the realms of particle physics and experiments with particle accelerators (Section 6.1.3), the search for evidence of inflation (Section 6.4) requires a deep understanding of quantum theory and current particle experiments could help to solve some of the Cosmological Problems. Then there are the telescopes that are not telescopes: the equipment that measures gravitational waves and cosmic rays.

All of these different techniques contribute to build up a picture of what the universe is like. Bit by bit we measure and test and theorise and measure again. As we get better equipment our measurements are getting more accurate, the distances we can see are getting further and the theories we can test are getting more complex. The technology we have today has led us into what we call the era of 'precision cosmology' (Section 6.8).

As we get more precise, we are finding discrepancies between measurements made with different techniques. The difference in the value of the Hubble constant from various measurement methods has become big enough that it now has a name: the Hubble tension (Section 6.5). Then there are the emerging differences between measurements of dark energy (Section 6.6). These differences are being called a 'cosmological crisis'. At the moment it is not so much a crisis as a discrepancy but as we get more accurate measurements maybe it will turn into a crisis, or it may go away. This chapter looks at the work astronomers are doing to answer the questions in cosmology and where the next Cosmological Clues will come from.

6.1.1 Surveys

Surveying objects in the sky is the core work of astronomers. We can survey the sky for the highest energy light, gamma rays and X-rays, through ultraviolet (UV), visible and infrared (IR) light, to the lowest energies of light, the microwaves and radio waves. Earth's atmosphere absorbs some of these wavelengths and it also blurs the light that it does let through. For this reason, telescopes are on Earth, some are placed on a balloon or a plane to be within a thin atmosphere and some are in space so that there is no atmosphere to interfere with the measurements. There is even a gold-plated telescope on the moon, placed there during the lunar landing in 1972, that took photographs of UV light and was used to show that interstellar gas (the gas between stars) is made up of molecules of hydrogen. In 2013, China sent another UV telescope to the moon (*Chang'e-3*) which beams back data on galaxies and hot bright objects.

Satellite telescopes are the most expensive telescopes but for some wavelengths they are the only option. Balloon-based telescopes are used for surveys that must be above the atmosphere and are cheaper than satellites. Ground-based telescopes are the most popular and there are many of them all over the World, often in areas where the air is dry (deserts) or where the air is thin (mountains), or both, which helps to reduce atmospheric interference. New radio telescopes are being built in radio quiet areas away from any people. Methods to adjust for the atmosphere on ground-based telescopes include complex adaptive optics and laser guides: shining lasers skywards to measure the atmosphere and adjust the optics to compensate.

Figure 6.1: The *Planck* satellite surveys the Cosmic Microwave Background (Artist's concept). Credit: ESA/NASA/JPL-Caltech.

Gamma Rays

Gamma rays were discovered in 1900 and the first telescopes were in the 1960s. In cosmology, gamma rays are used to hunt for dark matter from possible annihilations of dark matter particles giving off gamma rays. Gamma rays are light that have the shortest wavelength, and the highest energy, and are produced in radioactive decay of elements. Their wavelength is so short they can pass through atoms. They are also produced by cosmic rays (which are extremely fast moving particles from space) when they hit the atmosphere. Most gamma rays from space do not get through Earth's atmosphere so gamma ray astronomy is often based in space or balloons, although future detectors are likely to be on Earth to detect the most energetic gamma rays that interact in the atmosphere.

Gamma rays from space come from extreme environments such as emissions from supernova explosions and when black holes destroy stars at the centre of galaxies (active galactic nuclei). There are also gamma-ray bursts which are the most intense source of light known, lasting from 1 to 60 seconds. It is not known what causes these bursts, although it could possibly be when neutron stars and black holes merge or when a black hole is born following a supernova. One gamma-ray burst can contain the same energy as all the energy the Sun will give out in it's whole lifetime. There are various gamma-ray satellites in space: ESA's *INTEGRAL*, NASA's *SWIFT* and *Fermi GST*, the Italian *AGIE* and the Japanese *GAP*.

X-rays

X-rays have energies less than gamma rays, were discovered in 1895 and first used in astronomy in the 1950s. In space, they are produced in extremely hot gases and are used to study the remains of supernova explosions (particularly relevant for dark energy studies) and the hot gas in galaxy clusters that provides evidence for cluster dynamics and cosmic web formation. X-rays do not travel through the atmosphere so are detected from space or balloons. The Sun is a source of X-rays.

The NASA *Chandra X-ray Observatory* and ESA *XMM-Newton* satellite were both launched in 1999 and have been significant in providing X-ray survey data, including identifying black holes and galaxy clusters. Future X-ray satellites will look at magnetic fields in black holes, supernova and active galactic nuclei (NASA *IXPE* 2022), look at structure formation of the universe and dark matter (Japanese *XRISM* 2022) and map hot gas and give us more clues about the cosmic web (Europe/USA/Japan *ATHENA* 2031).

UV, Visible and Infrared Light

UV light was discovered in 1801 and has less energy than X-rays but more than visible. The universe viewed in UV looks different than in visible. The first astronomical UV detection was from the Sun in 1946 using a rocket-borne camera. UV light is given off by hot, young stars and dying stars that are growing hotter so we can use it to see where stars are in their evolution and to give us information on galaxy formation and evolution. UV light interacts with molecules, as we know when we get sunburn, and most of it is absorbed by the atmosphere so space or balloon based telescopes are required.

Visible light is a very narrow range of wavelengths and is the highest energy of light that can get through the atmosphere, that is why our eyes have evolved to see this light. Many telescopes use visible light and, since it is a narrow range, they often include infrared light as well.

Infrared (IR) light has lower energy than visible and, although it was discovered in 1800, it wasn't until the 1960s that IR was used seriously in astronomy. Visible light is blocked by dust in space but IR can see through the dust to objects that visible cannot. IR telescopes can see much further distances than visible and the VLT (very large telescope) has seen a galaxy that existed when the universe was just 470 million years old. The VLT could see both headlights of a car on the moon.

The same mirrors and lenses can be used for IR and visible light so they can be designed to do both. IR telescopes need to be kept cool (with liquid nitrogen) to reduce the background thermal IR that the telescopes themselves produce. Water vapour in the atmosphere absorbs specific wavelengths of IR, and emits IR, so the telescopes tend to be in high, dry places, such as the VLT in the Atacama desert in Chile and the GTC (Gran Telescopio Canarias) in the Canary Islands. Above the atmosphere are the *Spitzer Space Telescope*, the *Herschel Space Observatory* and SOFIA (Stratospheric Observatory for Infrared Astronomy) that is flown in a plane.

The *Hubble Space Telescope* (*HST*) was launched in 1990 and detects UV, visible and infrared light. It is one of the largest and most well known telescopes of recent times and has produced amazing images showing the wonder of the universe, as well as vast quantities of data that has been used for important science. *HST* has given us some of the most detailed images ever taken of galaxies and has also identified many new supernova that are used to measure the Hubble constant and dark energy.

The Dark Energy Survey (DES) has measured 300 million galaxies and, by measuring the distance to each galaxy, it gives clues on the evolution of galaxies, the cosmic web, dark energy and expansion and, as we look back far enough, it gives information on when the first stars formed (the Epoch of Reionisation).

Future telescopes are being planned that can look back even further, detect even more objects and look at even more detail of galaxies, clusters and supernova. Some of the planned satellite IR/visible telescopes are the NASA *James Web Space Telescope* in 2021, the ESA *Euclid* in 2022 and the NASA *Nancy Grace Roman Space Telescope* in 2025. Two large ground-based telescopes that are planned are the Vera Rubin Telescope and the ELT (Extremely Large Telescope).

Radio Waves

A radio wave is light that has a wavelength longer than infrared, starting at 1 millimetre and going to beyond 10,000 kilometres. Radio waves were predicted by James Clerk Maxwell in 1867 and radio astronomy started in 1931 when Karl Jansky discovered radio waves coming from the Milky Way. His name is used in the units measuring the strength of radio sources in astronomy.

Radio waves detect objects that are too cold to produce visible light and are used to detect neutral hydrogen atoms. This allows astronomers to study the cold clouds in interstellar space, distant galaxies back to when stars and galaxies first formed (Epoch of Reionisation) and molecular clouds where stars are born. Another source of radio waves comes from electrons moving in magnetic fields, called synchrotron radiation, that can be used to detect supernova remnants, pulsars and active galactic nuclei formed by black holes destroying the surrounding matter. Radio astronomy sees a lot of structure in galaxies that is not seen at other wavelengths.

Radio waves up to about 10-metre wavelength are not absorbed by the atmosphere and ground-based radio telescopes can be used. Telescopes need

Figure 6.2: SKA antennae. Artist's impression of the dishes that will make up the Square Kilometre Array to be placed in South Africa. They will form a radio interferometer, with another set of antennae set up in Australia. Credit: SKA Organisation/Swinburne Astronomy Productions.

to be bigger than the size of the wavelength of light being measured, so radio telescopes need to be very large. Traditionally, they have been dishes (like radars) and the largest single dish radio telescopes are the 500 m FAST (Five-Hundred Metre Aperture Spherical Telescope) in China (2016), the 305 m Arecibo Observatory in Puerto Rico (1963) and the 100 m Green Bank Telescope in USA (2002), the biggest fully steerable single dish radio telescope.

To improve the ability of radio telescopes to detect high resolution images a technique called radio interferometry was developed by Martin Ryle in 1946. Multiple dishes (or detectors) are spread out and linked together and the image can be recreated from the interference patterns that are formed. The size of the telescope becomes the largest distance between two antennas in the array. This also increases the amount of signal collected by the number of detectors used. Figure 6.2 shows a future radio interferometer (due 2025), the SKA (Square Kilometre Array), based in South Africa, with another set of antennas in Australia. Existing radio interferometers are ALMA (Atacama Large Millimeter Array) with 66 antennas spread over a 16 kilometre distance in Chile, ASKAP and MEERKAT (as part of the SKA project), and the

European LOFAR (Low-Frequency Array) with 20,000 antennae spread across Europe. Simultaneous observations from a satellite and ground based telescope can make a very long baseline telescope the size of the separation between them.

Microwaves and the CMB

Microwaves are a subset of radio waves with wavelengths between 1 millimetre and 1 metre. They play an important role in astronomy because it is the region that the Cosmic Microwave Background is seen (the CMB is brightest at 2 millimetres). There have been many telescopes that have surveyed the sky for the CMB, the key ones are the satellites *COBE* 1989–1993, *WMAP* 2001-2010 and *Planck* 2009-2013. These telescopes have measured the CMB temperature, the blackbody spectrum, the temperature fluctuations (anisotropies), the CMB gravitational lensing and the Sunyaev-Zel'dovich effect which can be used to identify distant galaxy clusters. From these CMB measurements the cosmological parameters have been determined.

Future CMB telescopes will be looking to improve the accuracy of these surveys and to look for polarisation modes of the CMB that may give clues for inflation. The next generation of CMB telescopes are called the CMB-S4 (Stage 4) and will be ground-based at the South Pole and the Atacama plateau in Chile planned for first light in 2029. The aim of CMB-S4 is to provide evidence for inflation by detecting the signature of primordial gravitational waves, to map dark matter in the universe, to determine neutrino mass, to look for limits on dark matter particles (axions), to improve dark energy measurements, and to test general relativity on large scales.

6.1.2 Computing

There is only one universe. We observe it's behaviour to work out how it works but we cannot experiment with other universes or observe another universe. That is until the invention of the modern computer. Cosmologists can now gather evidence through experimentation using computer simulations where alternative universes can be created to test theories and ideas and see if they match what is observed. This has opened up a whole new way of doing astronomy.

This is where we can improve our precision cosmology. With computers we can test out different models, create other universes and do experiments on them. This was never possible before, we had to observe what was there and make inferences. Now, we can compare what we see to other artificial universes. Such simulations need a lot of computing power and some require the use of supercomputers. Some of the significant computer cosmology simulations that have been produced are the Horizon Simulation, the Illustris TNG Project and the Millennium Simulation. Videos giving unique insights into the evolution of the universe are shown on their websites.

Astronomers also need computers to work the telescopes. Computers are used to clean the data from the telescopes, remove the atmospheric interference and any systematic issues from the telescope itself that need to be removed from the data. Images need to be cleaned and then they need to be catalogued. Computers can do this work but they are not as efficient as the human eye at identifying images. The general public are enlisted to help identify and catalogue images in citizen science projects at the Zooniverse website. Citizen science has become an important part of cataloguing images in surveys.

Current telescopes create so much data that astronomers cannot analyse it all, so we pick the data we want to use or have time to study. Future telescopes that are being developed will create even larger amounts of data: terabytes of data a second. The only way to analyse this data will be to use computers. For this we need ever more sophisticated methods; machine learning and artificial intelligence are some of the approaches being investigated to handle such large amounts of data. This is new technology and is a fusion of computing and astronomy that could lead to exciting results in both fields.

6.1.3 Experiments

Cosmology covers many aspects of physics and requires bringing in evidence from experiments that are not cosmology based but have an impact on how we view the universe. In the mid-20th century, experiments in nuclear physics provided the evidence for the Big Bang Nucleosynthesis model that explains how the elements formed in the early universe and also how the nuclear processes in stars work. Today, cosmology has led us into the realm of quantum theory and the experiments happening in this field are providing us with evidence that could answer some of the outstanding Cosmological Problems. These experiments use high energy particle accelerators in places such as CERN and Fermilab (see Figure 6.3).

Then there are the experiments that are designed to detect dark matter particles that use particle accelerators and include using Earth itself as a particle detector in projects such as IceCube. Using cosmic rays as a source of high energy particles from the sky is another type of experiment that provides clues for cosmology; it was using cosmic rays that the first antimatter particle, the positron, was discovered. There is a particle detector on the International Space Station (AMS-02) that can detect cosmic rays.

There are many other experiments that are investigating the complexity of quantum behaviour, some of which may shed light on what happened in the early universe. These experiments will not be discussed here but for cosmologists it is important that we know what clues these experiments are uncovering and, where appropriate, to apply the results to how the universe works. The overlap between astronomy and particle physics is the field of astroparticle physics and is now accepted as a distinct discipline in science.

Figure 6.3: ATLAS experiment at the Large Hadron Collider (LHC) CERN that is used to search for dark matter. Credit: ATLAS Experiment copyright 2020 CERN.

6.2 WHAT CLUES ARE WE LOOKING FOR?

In science, the projects, surveys and experiments that are being undertaken are dictated by the scientific questions that we would like to answer but they are also limited by what is possible to do. There are six important cosmological questions that are being worked on today that can provide evidence to turn ΛCDM from a model to a theory.

1. What is dark matter, where is it in the universe, and how much of it is there?

2. Can any evidence be found to confirm inflation?

3. How fast is the universe expanding and can the accuracy of the measurement of the Hubble constant be improved?

4. What is the strength of dark energy, does it change with time, and where does it originate from?

5. How and when did stars and galaxies form in the early universe and what impact does galaxy evolution make to the ΛCDM model?

6. Can improving the accuracy of the cosmological parameters provide further evidence for the ΛCDM model and answer some of the Cosmological Problems?

6.3 FINDING DARK MATTER

Where is Dark Matter and how much is there?

It is possible to measure where dark matter is in the universe using gravitational lensing. A map of dark matter across the whole sky is shown in Figure 6.4 and was produced using gravitational lensing of the CMB by the *Planck* Collaboration [107]. It is also possible to use gravitational lensing of galaxies to map dark matter. The KiDS (Kilo-Degree Survey) team [108] produced a dark matter map using gravitational lensing of 31 million galaxies and compared it with the *Planck* map. They found that they were not the same; the KiDS map was smoother than the *Planck* map by 10%. In ΛCDM, as the structure of matter forms, galaxies and clusters grow denser, the voids get bigger and the universe becomes more lumpy. Dark matter would be expected to have a smoother distribution in the earlier universe than the later universe. Since the CMB is an early universe measurement and galaxies a late universe measurement, then this result seems to be the wrong way round; we would expect the CMB to produce a smoother dark matter map. This may indicate that there is something else going on that is not included in the ΛCDM model. Future surveys, from telescopes such as the Vera Rubin and *Euclid*, may shed some light on this discrepancy.

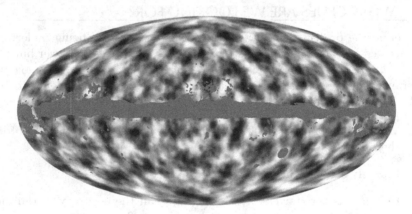

Figure 6.4: A map of dark matter across the whole sky produced from gravitational lensing of the CMB. Darker areas are where the dark matter is denser and the light areas have less dark matter. The solid grey strip across the centre has been blocked out and is where the light from the Milky Way would be. Image from Figure 19 by Planck Collaboration, 2014, "Planck 2013 results. XVII. Gravitational lensing by large-scale structure", *A&A*, 571, A17. Credit: ESA and the Planck Collaboration.

How much dark matter is in the universe can be measured using various techniques; from the fluctuations in the CMB, from galaxy cluster analysis, and from supernova measurements. The *Planck* CMB measurements give a value of 26.8% for the total energy dark matter density in the universe.

What is Dark Matter?

There are many projects that are searching for dark matter particles. They rely on three approaches; indirect detection, direct detection and creation of dark matter particles. Generally, they are either searching for the heavier WIMP particle or the lighter axion particle.

If dark matter interacts with atomic matter then it does so very weakly and to see even one interaction will require a lot of atomic matter for the dark matter to interact with. This could happen in the Sun, Earth, in the Milky Way or another galaxy, and we may be able to see the resulting shower of particles created when the dark matter annihilates. This is what the indirect searches are looking for, that elusive piece of evidence from the sky; a neutrino burst, gamma-ray burst or cosmic ray burst. These searches use satellite telescopes that look for the burst particles directly or ground-based experiments looking for the burst particles when they interact with the Earth's atmosphere.

The direct detection experiments are looking for dark matter that has interacted directly with the nuclei of atoms. As the nucleus breaks-up or recoils, signature light and particles such as electrons are given off. These experiments are usually performed deep underground to reduce the background noise.

If dark matter can annihilate into atomic particles then maybe the reverse is true and they can be created by high energy collisions between protons. These experiments are being performed in particle colliders, such as in the Large Hadron Collider at CERN, where extremely high energies can be produced by colliding protons together.

Direct detection of dark matter particles

- **Using xenon.** The XENON1T project ran from 2016 to 2018. It searched for dark matter particles from the sky that could interact with the nuclei of xenon atoms; they would annihilate and give off signature particles and light that can be detected. It can detect WIMPS, axions and neutrinos. Figure 6.5 is a photograph of the experiment. It is based at the Laboratori Nazionali del Gran Sasso (LNGS) in Italy with 1.4 kilometres of rock surrounding it to reduce the noise from unwanted interactions caused by cosmic rays. Xenon is only a liquid at very low temperatures so has to be kept at less than $-100°C$ and is highly purified to remove any contaminants and radioactivity. 3.2 tonnes of xenon are used in the experiment.

  Previous experiments with smaller amounts of xenon (LUX, Zeplin, PandaX) had not produced any evidence of dark matter. In 2020, there was much excitement when the XENON1T reported a possible event that could be an axion that came from the Sun. This has yet to be confirmed and may be background noise, but will be a breakthrough if it is a real event. Future projects with larger amounts of xenon are planned, including the XENONnT (8.3 tonnes of xenon) and the LuxZeplin Project (7

Figure 6.5: The XENON1T underground experiment. The tank on the left contains one tonne of cooled liquid xenon to detect dark matter interactions with the xenon nuclei. On the right is the building to service the experiment. Credit: The XENON1T project.

tonnes of xenon). The number of interaction events predicted to be detected by LuxZeplin is between 1 and 20 events a year.

- **Using argon.** There are also Argon based detectors searching for dark matter, such as DEAP-3600 using 3.6 tonnes of Argon and the planned DarkSide 20K experiment that will use 20 tonnes of argon.

- **Using crystal detectors.** Another direct detection approach is to use a scintillation crystal that gives off light when hit by charged particles. In 1998, the DAMA/LIBRA experiment observed an annual variation in the detected signals, peaking in June, and they have continued to see the variation for over 20 years. They propose that this is related to the Earth moving through the dark matter halo of the Milky Way. This result has yet to be confirmed by an independent experiment. A similar project, the COSINE-100 in Korea, has not detected the annual variation.

- **Using bubble chambers.** PICO uses superheated liquid and acoustic pulses which produce bubbles when particles pass through the liquid. It is based 2 kilometres underground in the SNOLAB in Canada.

Indirect detection of dark matter particles

The IceCube project is in the South Pole Neutrino Observatory (see Figure 6.6) and uses one cubic kilometre of the optically clear ice sheets as the matter for particle bursts from the sky to interact with. It looks for neutrinos and

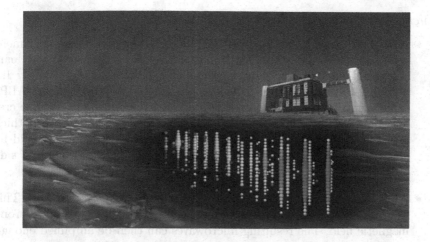

Figure 6.6: The IceCube detector is buried in the South Pole ice. A photo of the IceCube Lab containing the computers is visible above ground and an artistic rendering of neutrino event IC170922 is shown below Antarctica's surface. Credit: IceCube Collaboration/NSF.

possible dark matter annihilations. There are 86 cables drilled into the ice each holding 60 detectors at a depth between 1.5 and 2.5 kilometres. They detect interactions from high energy gamma rays and cosmic ray particles from the sky, energies that are a million times higher than nuclear reactions. IceCube detects 275 neutrinos and 275 million cosmic rays each day. Evidence of dark matter candidates is looked for via the neutrino bursts that could happen when dark matter annihilates in the Sun, Earth or galaxies. No candidate dark matter events have been detected yet. It is planned to upgrade the IceCube detectors and in the future to extend the volume to 10 cubic kilometres.

Creation of dark matter particles

CERN Large Hadron Collider and Fermilab. There are several ways that dark matter is being investigated using particle accelerators such as at CERN and Fermilab. The first is to create dark matter particles by colliding high energy protons together. The evidence for this would be 'missing energy' as a result of the dark matter particles taking some of the energy away that cannot be detected. No missing energy that could be dark matter has been detected so far. Another way is to look for evidence of supersymmetry (SUSY). Certain supersymmetry particles could be dark matter, in particular the neutralino. If there is evidence that supersymmetry particles exist then that could provide clues as to how to detect neutralinos and other supersymmetric particles. Evidence for supersymmetry could also provide evidence for some string theories, for inflation, and possibly solutions to the antimatter problem. So far no evidence for SUSY has been found.

Search for Axions

- **ALPS II** (Any Light Particle Search) in Germany. This experiment shines light through walls. Dark matter may not be heavy WIMP particles but may be very light particles called WISPs (very Weakly Interacting Sub-eV Particles). Axions are a type of WISP. In the ALPs experiment, laser light is passed through a strong magnetic field to create some axions. The light (and axions) are then shone onto a thick metal plate. The light is blocked by the plate but the axions would be able to pass through and be converted back into light on the other side of the barrier.

- **ADMX** (Axion Dark Matter eXperiment) in Washington State. This experiment seeks to convert axions into microwave light using a strong magnetic field. The resulting microwaves can then be amplified enough to be detected. The detector is so sensitive that if it was on another planet it could pick up mobile phone signals from Earth.

- **The CAST project** (CERN Axion Solar Telescope). This project looks for axions that could be coming from the Sun. These axions would have high energies and a strong magnetic field is used to convert the axions into X-rays for detection.

6.4 EVIDENCE FOR INFLATION

Inflation is a theory that is waiting for evidence. There is one prediction of inflation theory that could possibly be tested; inflation would have created waves in spacetime which we call primordial gravitational waves. There are two ways that we may be able to see these gravitational waves. The first is by the effects it would have left in the CMB and the second is the direct observation of the gravitational waves. These waves today would be very weak and have a very long wavelength so will be very difficult to detect but they are being searched for.

The first method is to look for polarised CMB light. When light is polarised it means the orientation of the electric field in the light is aligned in the same direction (the same way that sunglasses work). There are two types of CMB polarisation: E-modes and the weaker B-modes. Primordial gravitational waves from inflation would have affected the light of the CMB B-modes and left swirls in the direction of them. If these swirls could be detected then that would be evidence that inflation happened. The picture is complicated by another source of B-modes from the gravitational lensing of the E-modes. In 2002, the E-modes were observed by the DASI (Degree Angular Scale Interferometer) telescope. The B-modes created by the gravitational lensing of E-modes were detected in 2013 by the South Pole Telescope.

In 2014, there was much excitement when it was thought that the inflation B-modes had been found by the BICEP2 experiment but following the analysis

Figure 6.7: A still from a computer simulation of two black holes merging. The gravitational waves that emanate from the merger are seen by the distortions of the stars. Credit: The SXS (Simulating eXtreme Spacetimes) Project (http://www.black-holes.org).

of CMB data from the *Planck* satellite it was concluded that the signal was from light scattered by dust in the Milky Way. The search continues and there are now five BICEP2 telescopes combined together called the Keck Array which will be updated to four BICEP3 telescopes, called the BICEP Array. These are all based in the South Pole to reduce atmospheric interference. The Simons Array in the Atacama desert, Chile, is also looking for inflation B-modes. The CMB-S4 will also look for the same signal when it is ready in 2029.

The second method is detecting the primordial gravitational waves. Gravitational waves are produced by strong gravitational events such as black holes or neutron stars merging. Figure 6.7 shows an artists impression of gravitational waves formed in spacetime by two black holes merging. The waves travel at the speed of light and although they start out very strong, by the time they reach us they are very weak.

In 2015, LIGO (Laser Interferometer Gravitational-wave Observatory) detected gravitational waves that were produced by two black holes colliding 1.3 billion light-years away. The signal was 1,000 times smaller than the nucleus of an atom. The equipment to detect such a small signal consists of two long arms of 4 kilometres each arranged in the shape of an L (see Figure 6.8). A laser is shone through the arms and very slight variations in the two arms can be detected. There are two LIGO sites with identical set-ups, one in Washington State and the other 3,000 kilometres away in Livingston, Louisiana. The equipment is extremely sensitive to vibrations so only when a signal is seen at both sites can it be considered as being from a gravitational wave. There

Figure 6.8: Aerial view of the LIGO detector. Credit: The Virgo Collaboration/CCO 1.0.

are other gravitational wave detectors: VIRGO in Italy that has 3 kilometre arms; GEO600 in Germany with 600 metre arms; KAGRA in Japan with 3 kilometre underground arms; and another LIGO in India under construction.

The direct measurement of primordial gravitational waves may be possible with *LISA* (Laser Interferometer Space Antenna), a gravitational wave interferometer that is being planned for space in 2034. That is a long time to wait but scientists are patient and it would be worth it if they are found. The arms in space can be much greater distances than on Earth and there will be less interference from vibrations, making the measurement of even smaller signals possible. LISA will consist of three spacecraft each with two telescopes, two lasers and two test masses. These will be used to measure the expansion of the universe, to test general relativity and to search for primordial gravitational waves.

The search for evidence of inflation requires all the skills of astronomers and the techniques used are pushing the boundaries of technology. Detecting gravitational waves is new. It is an exciting new technique in the very early stages and has opened up a whole new way of doing astronomy. Not only could measuring gravitational waves give us evidence for inflation but it could be a revolution in astronomy.

6.5 HOW FAST IS THE UNIVERSE EXPANDING?

The Hubble constant determines how fast the universe is expanding and is one of the most important measurements for cosmology. It is used to calculate cosmological distances and times as well as being fundamental to gaining precise measurements of the cosmological parameters. There are three main ways of measuring the value of the present Hubble constant, H_0; using standard candles (Type Ia supernova and Cepheid variable stars), using BAOs and using the CMB temperature fluctuations. In the 1980s, the goal was to measure H_0 to a 10% accuracy and, by 2010, the goal was to reach 2%. Today, the accuracy of H_0 has improved beyond this to 0.6% using the CMB and 1.9% using standard candles. This is rewarding for cosmologists although it has also created another problem.

The value of H_0 should be the same whatever method is used to measure it. When the measurements had larger inaccuracies this was the case. As the measurements have become more accurate a difference has appeared. The CMB and BAO measurements give a lower value than the standard candle measurements. This is a problem for astronomers and we would like to know why this is happening. Is there something wrong with the measurements or the ΛCDM model, or maybe there is some new physics involved that we do not understand? This discrepancy between the value of H_0 from different measurement methods is known as the 'Hubble tension'.

In Figure 6.9 the value of H_0 is plotted when measured using different methods. You can see that the measurements fall into two separate regions. The lower value measurements, of around 67 km/s/Mpc, were taken using the BAO and CMB. These methods are based on the oscillations that happened in the 'early' universe. The higher value measurements, of around 73 km/s/Mpc, were taken using standard candles and result from effects that happened in the 'late' universe (star and galaxy formation). The real problem comes from the accuracy of each of the measurements which are shown by the grey horizontal lines. These lines do not overlap between the early and late measurements. This means that they are different values.

The first thing that scientists do when measurements do not agree is look for possible errors in the way the measurements are taken and in the interpretation of the results. Three possible ways that errors could have been introduced are; through the distance measurements, through our understanding of the physics of stars and supernova evolution, and through the particles that we have included in the CMB calculations (these change the size of the CMB fluctuations).

The Hubble tension may be a real effect so we may need to change our model. Five different ways of changing the model have been explored by Adam Riess [109] (their impact on H_0 are shown at the top of Figure 6.9):

- Dark energy can change in time (quintessence).

- There can be an additional dark energy in the early universe.

- Change the type of particles in the early universe by adding another type of neutrino, for example sterile neutrinos.

- Allow dark matter to interact with atomic matter

- Change the flatness of the universe which changes how it expands.

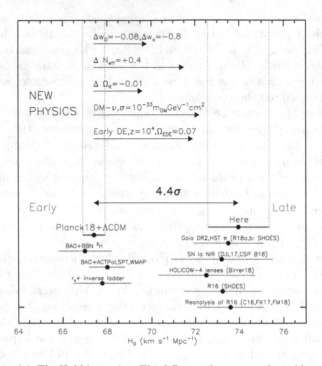

Figure 6.9: The Hubble tension: The difference between early and late universe measurements of H_0. At the top are possible differences in H_0 that could come from changing the ΛCDM model: time-varying dark energy, additional neutrinos, non-flat curvature, interactions between dark and atomic matter, and additional dark energy in the early universe. 'Here' is the measurement from the Riess et al 2019 paper that the figure is taken from. Credit: From Figure 4 by Riess et al, 2019, "Large Magellanic Cloud cepheid standards provide a 1% foundation for the determination of the Hubble constant and stronger evidence for physics beyond ΛCDM", *Astrophysical Journal*, 876, 85.

There are other ways that are being investigated to measure the Hubble constant including gravitational lensing of quasars (the H0liCOW project), using galaxy clusters, and using gravitational waves. As we get more measurements, the Hubble tension will either resolve itself or it may produce some new discovery or physics that will explain why there is a difference. Either way, the reason behind the Hubble tension is a question that we would like to get an answer to.

6.6 UNDERSTANDING DARK ENERGY

To find out more about dark energy we want to measure how the universe has expanded over time. From this we can determine it's strength and whether it has changed, and maybe get some clues as to what dark energy is. We explore the history of expansion by looking back in time at the most distant galaxies and at the CMB, the furthest point we can see. The techniques to measure the expansion history are mostly the same as the techniques we use to measure the Hubble constant and having a more accurate H_0 value will improve our dark energy measurements as we compare the value of expansion today with that of the past.

The main difficulty with understanding dark energy is that we cannot see it directly, we measure it's effects on other things, mainly the positions of stars (from supernova), galaxies (from the BAOs) and the structure within the cosmic web (from the shape of voids). What complicates the picture is that there are other processes that also affect galaxy distribution and the cosmic web and we have to unpick the dark energy effects from the others.

BAOs are a standard ruler within the universe and the BAOs in the distribution of increasingly distant galaxies can give us one of the most reliable measurements of how dark energy has affected the expansion history. To make these measurements we need to know the distance of millions of galaxies. The Dark Energy Survey (DES) measured the distance to 300 million galaxies going back as far as 9 billion years. It also detected 200,000 galaxy clusters for cluster counts and 207 supernova to use as standard candles.

Dark energy can also be detected using voids in the cosmic web. Voids are cosmic bubbles in the universe, regions where there are very few galaxies, and the effect of expansion on voids is relatively simple (compared to dense regions). By looking at how the shape, size and number of voids change with time it is possible to gather information about the expansion of the universe as well as other cosmological parameters. Surveys of large areas of the sky are needed to map the voids.

What the results are uncovering is a discrepancy between the dark energy measurements from the CMB and those from supernova. As with the Hubble tension there seems to be a difference between the early universe measurements and the late universe measurements. The difference is not as much as for the Hubble tension but it is enough for scientists to want to know what is causing it. Current and future surveys (the Vera Rubin, LOFAR, SKA and *Euclid*) will detect even larger numbers of galaxies, out to even further distances, from which we can test the discrepancy, test quintessence and other dark energy models.

6.7   HOW DO GALAXIES AFFECT COSMOLOGY?

In cosmology, we treat the universe as one system where there are particles that gravitate together within an expanding space. On the large scale and in the early universe this works very well. On a scale the size of galaxies there are more complex processes happening that affect the way the universe behaves and complicates our cosmology models; the formation and evolution of galaxies are more difficult to model and predict. As the accuracy of cosmology has improved the effects of galaxy evolution has become more important.

We would like to understand what these effects are and how they influence cosmology. To do this we need to understand more about galaxy evolution.

The way galaxy evolution affects how the structure of matter evolves has to be taken into account when making cosmology measurements. As structure grows the baryonic acoustic oscillations (BAOs) in the distribution of galaxies are stretched and affect measurements of expansion, dark energy and cosmological parameters. Galaxies tend to grow where the dark matter is, we call this 'bias', and also has to be taken into account when measuring BAOs. We would like to know more about the bias between where galaxies and dark matter exist.

As we look back in time there is a period when star formation was at it's peak when the universe was about 3.5 billion years old. This period is known as the cosmic noon. The universe was three times smaller and 27 times denser than it is now and galaxies were closer together. Images from the *Hubble Space Telescope* show that galaxies were smaller and had clumpy, irregular shapes. Today, galaxies are bigger and have regular, smooth shapes. A prediction of the Big Bang is that the universe would have looked different in the past and these *HST* observations confirm this prediction providing another Cosmological Clue.

The universe was also much brighter at cosmic noon. Theory says that stars were much bigger and shone more brightly than the lower mass stars of today. Stars prefer to form in spiral type galaxies and yet most of the galaxies today are elliptical shaped (spheroids). How and when did this change happen? We would like to know more about what the galaxies looked like then and how they evolved into the galaxies of today. Since galaxies were closer together mergers would have been more likely to occur and this is one way that bigger, smoother galaxies could have formed, although, evidence from computer simulations shows that the processes are more complex than this.

Going further back in time we come to the cosmic dawn, this is the name given to when stars first started to form at about 150–400 million years from the Big Bang. When the first stars formed they were massive stars that gave off a lot of strong UV light. This light was absorbed by the neutral hydrogen atoms, releasing electrons and creating ionised hydrogen. A bubble of ionised hydrogen formed around the stars and over a period of about a billion years these bubbles grew and merged until the universe was fully ionised and became transparent to light, which is why we can see the stars and galaxies today. This process is called reionisation and the time it took from the first ionised bubbles to all the universe being ionised is called the 'Epoch of Reionisation' (EoR). We cannot see stars this far back but there are other ways we can detect when the cosmic dawn happened using the CMB. Light at specific wavelengths are missing from the CMB and this can be used to determine when reionisation started.

We are able to see galaxies within the Epoch of Reionisation; deep galaxy surveys can detect galaxies when the universe was less than a few billion years old. The most distant galaxy observed by *HST* is when the universe was 400 million years old. The observation of this galaxy has caused a puzzle because theory predicts that galaxies should form later than this. Maybe there is some physics happening that has not been included in our models. As we look back further and further we can study the detail of what happened. Information from the CMB is just a snapshot in cosmic history. By studying galaxies through the whole epoch we can get a more detailed three-dimensional picture of how the primordial fluctuations evolved into the cosmic web.

The early phase of galaxy formation is not well understood. Protogalaxies are the precursors to galaxies. Identifying protogalaxies is not easy. They formed a long time ago and are very large, diffuse structures and we have questions about them that could help us understand the formation of structure. Did these protogalaxies form from dark matter collapsing with stars and black holes forming all at the same time, or was it more complex than this? Did dark matter halos merge together before stars could form, did protogalaxies exist before the stars formed, and what role did star formation have in developing the galaxy structures?

With future radio telescopes it may be possible to see even further back into the dark ages before the first stars formed. There is one specific wavelength of light at 21 centimetres that is emitted by neutral hydrogen. During the dark ages this light will have been emitted. It will be a tiny signal but if it can be detected then it may tell us something about the environment that existed before the first stars formed.

There is much to learn about how the evolution of stars and galaxies affects the universe, both in the early years and their continuing influence today. We still have many questions about the early formation of structure in the universe and studying distant galaxies could provide some answers to these questions. Finding such distant galaxies and understanding the dark ages, cosmic dawn and cosmic noon requires extremely sensitive telescopes and clever use of the light that interacts with atoms. Searching in the early universe uses all the skills of astronomers and the results will provide essential clues on how stars and galaxies influenced the evolution of the universe.

6.8 IMPROVING THE COSMOLOGICAL PARAMETERS

The combination of theoretical developments in the ΛCDM model and wide-ranging observational surveys has resulted in a set of cosmological parameters that define the ΛCDM model to a high degree of accuracy; this is precision cosmology. Most of the ten (and more) cosmological parameters that define the model are known to a level of 1% or better and we would like to improve this. There are some parameters where it is difficult to separate the values, they depend on each other, so we would like more evidence to enable us to separate them out.

The most powerful source for defining the cosmological parameters comes from CMB data. The set of parameters from the *Planck* team in 2018 is the current benchmark. These combine the CMB data with the data from BAOs as a separate and complimentary measurement technique and together they improve the accuracy of the parameters.

The cosmological parameters cover all aspects of cosmology and improving them requires all the techniques that have been discussed in this chapter: dark matter particle experiments, dark energy supernova surveys, large area galaxy surveys to detect the expansion rate from BAOs, wide area surveys to explore the cosmic web voids, X-ray measurements of clusters, gravitational lensing detection of dark matter and computer modelling to pull all the information together into a parameter set. New experiments and survey methods will improve the accuracy of cosmological parameters and provide more stringent tests of the ΛCDM model.

There are many ways that ΛCDM is being tested, questions being answered and Cosmological Problems being solved. It is an interesting time to be an astronomer as new telescopes and experiments come online. Each new telescope, particle detector, experiment and computer simulation adds to our understanding of how the universe works. There is plenty of work to do to test theories, discoveries to make and a universe to explore.

CHAPTER 7

The Future

Will the universe end?
The Scientific Process: CONCLUSION

"To see a World in a Grain of Sand, And a Heaven in a Wild Flower, Hold
Infinity in the palm of your hand, And Eternity in an hour"
William Blake, Auguries of Innocence

7.1   WHAT IS THE FUTURE OF THE UNIVERSE?

For most of human history it has been assumed that the universe will go
on forever, never changing. The individual stars and galaxies will change, be
born, evolve and die, but the overall structure of the universe on a large scale,
the scale of the cosmic web, will look the same wherever we look and whenever
we look: in the past, in the present and in the future. If we accept the Steady
State Theory of the universe then this is the future we will have. The Steady
State Theory says that the universe has been here forever and will continue
forever.

   This is not how the universe will end if we accept the Standard Model of
Cosmology (ΛCDM). In this model the universe does not stay the same but
evolves and changes as it cools down, it will look different in the future. How
it will look we cannot be sure but we have some theories; quite a few theories.
Seven possible futures are discussed and are shown conceptually in Figure 7.1.

   1. **Big Chill**. There are two opposing forces working on the overall struc-
      ture of the universe: the expansion due to the Big Bang and dark energy,
      and gravity pulling matter together causing contraction. If the expan-
      sion of the universe is pushing the universe apart faster than gravity is
      pulling the universe together then the universe will carry on expanding
      forever in what is called the 'big chill'. As the universe expands it will get
      colder and galaxies will get further apart until eventually all the matter
      that exists will be in isolated clusters and galaxies, no longer able to

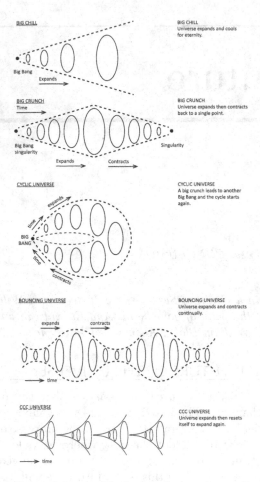

Figure 7.1: Some of the possible futures of our universe. Credit: C. Devereux and P. Farrell.

merge and form new stars. The cosmic web will be vastly spread out. The universe will be a cold, empty space with isolated lumps of matter.

2. **Big Rip**. We can take the model further. All objects could be ripped apart by the increasing expansion and the particles will no longer be able to interact. There will be no stars and planets just individual particles floating around in an ever expanding space. This was proposed by Robert Caldwell in 2003 [110] and is called the 'big rip' because all matter is ripped apart.

3. **Big Freeze**. We can take the model even further still. Not only could all objects be ripped apart during the expansion but time itself could stop. This is the 'big freeze'. It can be envisaged that the universe could

reach a point where all the particles are spread out uniformly and have reached a maximum amount of disorder (scientists call this entropy). At this point the universe can be considered as being frozen in time. There is movement but nothing changes. Everywhere would look the same and continue to look the same always. Since we measure time by how things change relative to something else, then time can be considered as having stopped. It can be argued that the point that time has stopped is the end of the universe.

4. **Big Crunch**. Instead of the universe forever expanding we could get the opposite. If the amount of matter in the universe has a greater gravitational pull than the expansion has a push, then the universe will eventually stop expanding and start to contract. As it contracts it will become smaller until it goes back to how the universe started, a singularity, all matter and energy at a single point. This is the 'big crunch'.

5. **Cyclic Universe**. In a future where the universe collapses to a singularity it does not necessarily mean that the universe ends there, it could be the beginning again. The universe resets itself and another Big Bang comes from the singularity and a new universe is born. The process of expanding, collapsing and exploding happens again and again in a continual loop. This 'cyclic universe' was proposed by Paul Steinhardt and Neil Turok in 2002 [76] whilst working on string theory. The universe expanding and contracting could last forever or it could eventually collapse into a final singularity.

6. **Bouncing Universe**. The models that I have outlined so far have all required a singularity. The laws of physics break down at singularities, so we don't like to have them in our models. If we have a model for the universe that allowed us to not have a singularity that would take away a problem. There are some possible universes that do not need singularities.

As far back as 1954, William Bonnor [111] proposed a universe that bounced between an expanding state and a contracting state without any Big Bangs or big crunches. He wanted a universe that is eternal and has no singularities, meaning no Big Bangs. If the universe has enough matter in it then it will stop expanding and start contracting. As it contracts it will heat up again and light could be converted into matter providing an expanding pressure again. The universe then bounces between expanding and contracting like an oscillating wave.

A more recent proposal of the bouncing model came out of string theory by Anna Ijjasa and Paul Steinhardt in 2019 [112]. In this model the universe does not shrink to a singularity but stays a finite size which then becomes the beginning of the new universe. The difference with this model is that the new universe keeps the information on the distribution of matter from the previous universe. They call this model an 'ekpyrotic universe' named after the ancient Greek view that the universe is in a cycle of being destroyed by fire and then reborn.

7. **Conformal Cyclic Cosmology (CCC).** One of the problems with any model that is not infinitely expanding (crunch, cyclic, bouncing) is that they break the second law of thermodynamics. This important law states that everything in the universe slowly becomes more disordered. An example of this is when we break a cup into many pieces it has become more disordered. The process does not work the other way though, the broken cup does not become whole again unless we fix it and then we are creating more disorder elsewhere in the energy we are using to fix it. The problem with a contracting universe is that it is becoming more ordered and so it breaks the second law of thermodynamics. There is also a problem with the Big Bang and the second law. If the universe is become increasingly disordered as it expands then it must have been exceedingly well ordered at the Big Bang. In 2005, the British mathematician Roger Penrose [113] proposed a radical idea for a cyclic universe that he called 'conformal cyclic cosmology' (CCC). This model says that the universe is infinitely expanding but that it will reach a point where matter is so spread out that the universe 'forgets' how big it is and 'forgets' time and it resets itself. The starting point of the new universe now looks the same as the old infinitely expanding universe, the values of the cosmological parameters that define the universe reset themselves and a new beginning happens. This model does not require a singularity and it allows for disorder to be continually increasing so does not break the second law of thermodynamics. It also does not need a very well ordered universe at it's beginning. It solves three problems with one theory but it is speculative.

How the universe will end is not clear, it is a topic of debate and research and depends on the model of cosmology that is used. The current accepted view of the end of the universe, based on the Standard Model of Cosmology, that the universe will expand forever producing the big chill. However, even in the standard model the big chill prediction is based on measurements on the amount of matter in the universe (dark matter and atomic matter), the rate of expansion of the universe (Hubble's constant), and the measured value of the acceleration of the expansion (dark energy). These measured values are being refined and we may find that they produce a universe that will stop expanding and start collapsing again. It could collapse all the way back until it reaches a single point again, producing the big crunch. There is also the possibility that the universe will expand and contract and then expand again, resulting in a cyclic universe or a bouncing universe that may continue forever. It could be that a modified gravity theory shows that the universe is in a steady state and will continue forever as it is.

So, the answer to how will the universe end is that it could continue forever as it is, either in a steady state or bouncing continually, or it could expand forever to become a cold nothingness, or reset itself to create another universe, or it could contract back to a single point with the possibility of another Big Bang exploding to create a new universe. Predictions into the future are by their very nature speculative but as scientists we like to be able to predict the outcome of our experiments and observations based on the laws of physics. At the moment we don't have enough evidence to make a good prediction. Although we are not going to be around to find out what does happens to the universe, we would like to have a model that gives us a clear prediction even if we can never test it to it's final conclusion. To get to a single prediction we need to get more evidence by measuring more accurately the values of mass and expansion in the universe so that we can predict to a high probability what will happen to the universe in the future.

What do we think is the most likely future? The best model we have at the moment is the ΛCDM Standard Model of Cosmology with well measured values that fit the model. If we take this model and extrapolate it to the future then the values we have measured today tell us that the universe will end with a big chill. It will expand forever with the galaxies getting increasingly further away from each other until eventually we will not be able to see the light from those galaxies. If the galaxies stay together then the Milky Way may still exist although now it will have merged with the Andromeda galaxy and probably other galaxies. Most of the stars will probably be cold and dead with just some small stars giving out the last of their light. What we won't be able to see is any other galaxies, even with the largest telescopes, because the light from those galaxies will be too far away to get to us. The galaxies will be outside our observable universe. The big chill leaves the universe as a cold, dark place. A chilling prospect, and not one I like the sound of, but it is what the science is telling us.

7.2   HOW WILL EARTH AND LIFE END?

To know when life is likely to end on Earth we have to know how the Earth will end. This will be when the Sun dies (unless the Earth gets hit by a massive asteroid before then). So when will the Sun die? The Sun will start to die in about 5 billion years time and take another 2 billion years to finally end. There is no supernova explosion and no black hole forming, that happens to larger stars at least eight times bigger than the Sun. What will happen is that the Sun will expand into a massive red giant and then end up as a tiny white dwarf. Although the picture is not as simple as this.

During the Sun's life, it gradually heats up making it brighter and giving out more energy. The younger Sun was 20–25% less bright than today. As it continues to get brighter it will heat up the Earth and there will come a point when life will end. In about 300 million years time, the Sun will have heated the Earth by 5°C and life will have to adapt to that. By 600 million years the atmosphere will not be able to sustain most life although there may be a few specialised plants. In 1 billion years, when the Sun is 67% brighter, the Earth will be 16°C hotter and the oceans will have started to evaporate and the only life left may be some microbes. In 2 to 3 billion years the Earth's magnetic field will disappear along with any possible remaining vestiges of life. At 4 billion years the surface of the Earth is likely to be molten. By the time the Sun starts to die in 5 billion years, the Earth's surface will be 600°C and everything on it will have been vaporised.

The Sun creates it's energy by nuclear fusion of hydrogen in it's core. This produces helium which is heavier than hydrogen. The helium moves towards the centre making the core heavier, the gravity stronger and the core shrinks becoming more dense. The denser core gets hotter, heating up the surrounding hydrogen which gets bigger so that the surface of the Sun gets cooler. This results in a Sun with a smaller, hotter core and a bigger, cooler surface. Slowly, over billions of years, the Sun gets brighter as it gets hotter and bigger as the hydrogen moves outwards. Eventually after about 6 billion years, the supply of hydrogen will start to run low and the Sun will cool, turning red, and significantly expand to become a red giant. In about 7 billion years, the red giant Sun will be massive, giving out much more energy than it does today and be 2,300 times brighter. The outer edges of the red giant Sun will have first reached Mercury and Venus and burnt them up, and may possibly have reached Earth.

The Sun then does a few interesting things quite quickly. It shrinks again to about 2% of it's red giant size, getting 10% hotter and turning orange. It then grows again in a second red giant phase, this time getting even bigger to reach beyond Jupiter. It then shrinks and expands another four or five times, repeating the cycle every 1,000 years. Each time it grows, some of the outer layers of the Sun are blown away and eventually chunks of the Sun break off as the gravity gets less. After the final expansion, about 45% of the mass of the Sun will have been blown away out of the Solar System. Only the core of the Sun will be left. It will be the size of Earth and extremely hot, emitting X-rays and UV light. It will be a white dwarf. There are no more nuclear reactions, just the glowing embers of a dying star. The white dwarf Sun will slowly cool and it will take about 100 billion years for it to stop emitting light and become a black dwarf. You may think that there must be lots of black dwarfs in the universe from all the dead stars, but there are none. No black dwarfs exist today because there has not been enough time since the beginning of the universe for one to form.

When the Earth ends can humans continue to survive? For that to happen we will need go to another planet that orbits another star. This raises the question of whether we can travel to other planets and what it would be like to live there. There is active development of spaceships to take humans to Mars for the first time. Mars is a bleak barren planet where we may be able to survive using our ability to create technology that will allow us to exist permanently indoors or underground to avoid the radiation. It will not be pleasant living there. You will not be able to go outside without a space suit and feel the wind and paddle in water, the radiation would kill you, there is no liquid water, and although the winds are not too strong there are regular massive dust storms. What we may gain from going to Mars is learning how to live on another planet.

What about going to a planet orbiting another star (an exoplanet)? First we have to find another suitable planet. We have 300 million years to find one and leave. The nearest star is Proxima Centauri at a distance of 4 light-years away, that means it would take us 4 years if we travelled at the speed of light, although physics tells us this is impossible. Using today's technology it would take us over 70,000 years to get there. In 2016 [3], an Earth size planet was found orbiting our closest star, Proxima Centauri, and it lives in the habitable zone of the star which means that liquid water could exist there. This exoplanet is called Proxima b. There may be some atmosphere on Proxima b although it could have been blown away by the solar winds from the star. This may turn out to be a planet worth going to (although it is not looking likely) and we would need much more evidence before we set off to go there. We should not rule out the possibility that we may develop a technology, using some physics that we do not yet know, that would allow us to travel to Proxima b in a spaceship over a period of hundreds of years, but it is not something we will be able to do in the foreseeable future. Alternatively, we have to develop the technology to allow us to live in spaceships for at least 70,000 years. This is a long time, especially considering humans have been on Earth for only 200,000 years. It is such a long time that evolution will happen in these spaceships.

The death of the Sun will definitely be the end of the Earth, but life on Earth will have ended well before then, for humans it could be less than 300 million years. If we are careful with the planet maybe we can survive another 300 million years but it is much more likely that life on our planet ends before that. The more likely outcome is that life ends through our poor choices of how we treat the planet; we use up it's resources, heat it up, inject it with artificial chemicals and suffocate it with plastic. A pretty tortuous way to treat the planet that sustains us.

7.3 IS THE SCIENTIFIC PROCESS THE KEY TO OUR FUTURE?

Changing our understanding of the universe has changed how we as humans see ourselves. Once we saw ourselves at the centre of the universe, everything revolved around us as the most important objects that exist. Now we see ourselves as an insignificant speck – animals on a small rock, going round a small sun, on the outer edges of a small galaxy, which is in a small group of galaxies, with billions and billions of other galaxies in the universe. We think we are probably not the only life in the universe. We also think that we are unlikely to ever meet any other life if it exists, the distances are too great to ever meet them. We know we have only one planet to live on. Maybe we can go to Mars, but it will be a harsh environment and not much fun to live there.

Maybe, going to another planet will be possible in thousands or millions of years but it is unlikely to be anywhere near as good as this one, after all we have evolved to live here. We know that we have to look after the Earth we have.

I watched a magpie walking through the grass finding food, listening to other birds, looking for danger, and then fly into the trees. In this one scene there is all of the history of the universe and all of what we need to know about our planet. Without the magpie we are poorer, without the trees we cannot survive. The magpie exists because of the Big Bang creating the basic elements, and gravity pulling them together into stars, and nuclear reactions giving us light and heat from the stars, and a supernova explosion giving us the heavy elements, iron and all the metals that went into our planet, and the iron forming a core in the Earth that creates a magnetic field to stop the damaging radiation from the sun so that chemical reactions can happen and life can form and the magpie can sing in the trees with me watching it.

Understanding how the universe evolved has given us the knowledge that we live on a planet that is probably not unique, but that the creation of life on the planet is fragile. Many things had to come together to create life on Earth. Science has enabled us to understand this and it has also given us the ability to understand that we have put this in danger. There is no other life in the universe that will come to save us when things go wrong, we have to do it ourselves. New technology is likely to come up with some of the answers, but that alone will not save the planet. We also have to change the way we live.

Life has evolved as a result of the universe evolving and humans have evolved with the power to think and change the World based on that thinking. We have to be cleverer in our thinking if we want to keep life on Earth. So how can we do this? We can improve how we make decisions. If we based our decisions on evidence, and then tested the results of our decisions by getting more evidence, and then stopped the things that are not working and improved the things that are working – so if we use scientific thinking – then maybe we can change our way of living so that it works for the planet and for us, as humans in a technological age. In that way, by using scientific thinking, maybe cosmology can save the planet.

Timeline of Clues

The next three pages contain a timeline of the Cosmological Clues from 1900 to 2020 that are discussed in this book. There are a few points of interest I would like to highlight.

Although the period from 1900 to 1920 does not have many Cosmological Clues it was a very active period for laying down the fundamental theories of modern physics that cosmology relies upon today. The laws of gravity were revolutionised by Einstein's theory of relativity (which appears on the timeline) and also quantum theory was born during this period (also developed by Einstein and for which he won the Nobel prize in 1921). With theories of inflation and the need to solve the Dark Matter Problem and the Antimatter Problem, quantum theory has become as important to cosmology as it is to all other physics disciplines. The clues for quantum theory are not included in this timeline.

It is noticeable that during and after the Second World War there was not much astronomy activity and the new clues that were developed during that time were to do with nuclear processes, the theory of which was advanced significantly due to the interest in developing a nuclear bomb. Fred Hoyle and George Gamow were important players in applying the new nuclear physics to cosmology.

The last 40 years has been a very active one for cosmology and many new clues have been found. The more recent period may seem less active but this is a reflection that often time is needed to determine if the clue is real and the impact it has on cosmology. There will be many clues being worked on today that are likely to appear on a future timeline.

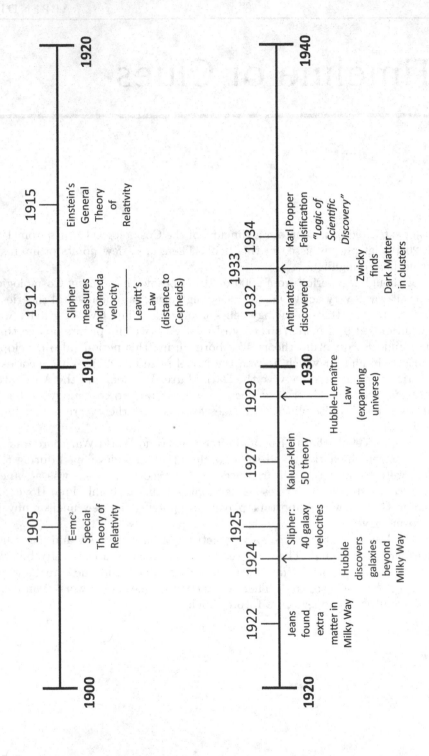

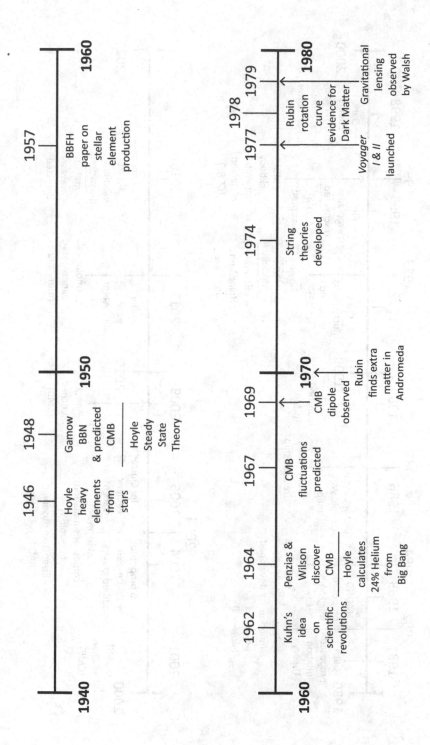

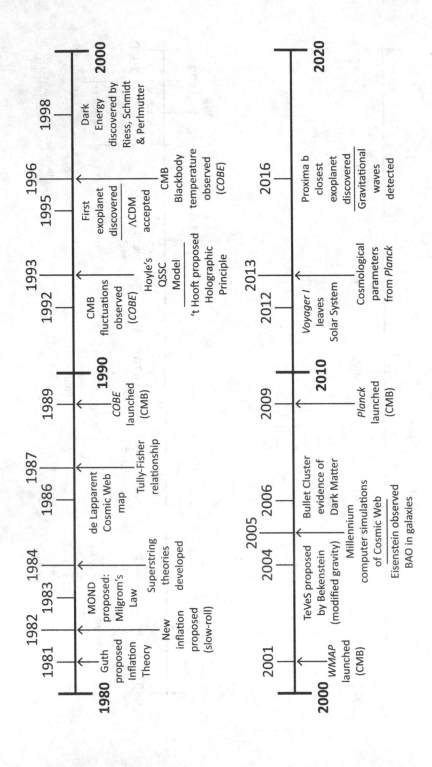

Glossary

Atomic matter Also called baryonic matter, visible matter, ordinary matter and known matter. It is the matter in the universe that we can see in the stars, galaxies, gas and dust. It makes up about 15% of all the matter in the universe.

Baryonic Acoustic Oscillations (BAO and standard ruler) Oscillations of matter in the very early universe that created the temperature fluctuations in the CMB and a distinct distance that galaxies prefer to be apart from each other which can be used as a 'standard ruler' to measure expansion of the universe. Today this BAO distance is 490 million light-years.

Big Bang Nucleosynthesis (BBN) The creation of the first chemical elements, mostly hydrogen and helium, within the first few minutes after the Big Bang.

Cepheid variable stars A type of pulsating star that has a well defined relationship between timings of the pulses and brightness. It is used to determine the distance to galaxies and is an important rung on the cosmology distance ladder.

Cosmic Microwave Background (CMB) Uniform background light seen across the whole universe that was produced when atoms first formed 380,000 years after the Big Bang. We see it today as microwave radiation at a temperature of 2.7K and wavelength of 2 millimetres.

Cosmic Web The large scale structure of the universe observed by the distribution of galaxies. It looks like a three-dimensional spiders web and consists of galaxy clusters (nodes), walls, sheets, filaments, and voids (holes) where there are very few galaxies.

Dark matter halos The dark matter that exists in a uniform sphere around galaxies. It generally goes out to much larger diameter than the visible galaxy.

General theory of relativity Einstein's theory of gravity states that gravity is the curvature of spacetime. Matter curves space-time and the curvature of spacetime makes matter move. It is a fundamental theory used in cosmology.

Gravitational lensing Light is deflected by the gravitational attraction of very large masses such as galaxies and galaxy clusters, which act as gravitational lenses. This effect is also seen in the CMB.

Redshift Galactic redshift (Doppler shift): an object moving away from us emits light that has a longer wavelength (is redder) than if it was stationary. Cosmological redshift: the increase in wavelength of light due to the expansion of the universe.

Standard candle An object in the sky, such as a supernova or Cepheid star, that has a known brightness. The distant to these objects can be calculated and are an important part of the cosmological distance ladder.

Standard Model of Cosmology (ΛCDM) Also called the Lambda Cold Dark Matter model. The Standard Model of Cosmology provides an explanation of the evolution of the universe. It is based on the Big Bang, the expansion of the universe, cold dark matter, and dark energy.

Standard Model of Particle Physics The theory that describes the behaviour of fundamental particles and three of the fundamental forces (electromagnetism, weak nuclear force, and strong nuclear force). It is a very accurate model based on quantum field theory. It includes baryons (protons and neutrons) and leptons(electrons and neutrinos).

Supernova A massive explosion of a dying star that produces the heavy elements in the universe. Type Ia are a particular type of supernova that are used as a standard candle to measure distance to galaxies.

Bibliography

[1] J. Ostriker and P. Steinhardt, "The observational case for a low-density Universe with a non-zero cosmological constant," *Nature*, vol. 377, no. 6, pp. 600–602, 1995.

[2] M. Mayor and D. Queloz, "A Jupiter-mass companion to a solar-type star," *Nature*, vol. 378, pp. 355–359, 1995.

[3] G. Anglada-Escude, P. Amado, J. Barnes, et al, "A terrestrial planet candidate in a temperate orbit around Proxima Centauri," *Nature*, vol. 536, pp. 437–440, 2016.

[4] A. M. Ghez, S. Salim, S. D. Hornstein, A. Tanner, J. R. Lu, M. Morris, E. E. Becklin, and G. Duchêne, "Stellar Orbits around the Galactic Center Black Hole," *Astrophysical Journal*, vol. 620, no. 2, pp. 620–744, 2005.

[5] N. F. Martin, R. A. Ibata, M. Bellazzini, M. J. Irwin, G. F. Lewis, and W. Dehnen, "A dwarf galaxy remnant in Canis Major: the fossil of an in-plane accretion onto the Milky Way," *MNRAS*, vol. 348, p. 12, 2004.

[6] B. Tully and R. Fisher, *Nearby Galaxy Atlas*. Cambridge Uni. Press, 1987.

[7] V. M. Slipher, "The radial velocity of the Andromeda nebula," *Lowell Observatory Bulletin*, vol. 1, pp. 56–57, 1913.

[8] H. S. Leavitt and E. C. Pickering, "Periods of 25 Variable Stars in the Small Magellanic Cloud," *Harvard College Observatory Circular*, vol. 173, pp. 1–3, 1912.

[9] E. Hubble, "A relation between distance and radial velocity among extra-galactic nebulae," *PNAS*, vol. 15, no. 3, pp. 168–173, 1929.

[10] G. Lemaître, "Un Univers homogene de masse constante et de rayon croissant rendant compte de la vitesse radiale des nebuleuses extra-galactiques," *Annales de la Societe Scientifique de Bruxelles*, vol. 47, pp. 49–59, 1927.

[11] H. Robertson, "Dynamical space-times which contain a conformal Euclidean 3-space," *Trans. Amer. Math. Soc.*, vol. 29, no. 3, pp. 481–496, 1927.

[12] F. Zwicky, "Die Rotverschiebung von extragalaktischen Nebeln," *Helvetica Physica Acta*, vol. 6, pp. 110–127, 1933.

[13] J. H. Jeans, "The motions of stars in a Kapteyn universe," *MNRAS*, vol. 82, pp. 122–132, 1922.

[14] J. Kapteyn, "First attempt at a theory of the arrangement and motion of the sidereal system," *Astrophysical Journal*, vol. 55, p. 302, 1922.

[15] J. Oort, "The force exerted by the stellar system in the direction perpendicular to the galactic plane and some related problems," *Bull. Astron. Inst. Netherlands*, vol. 6, p. 249, 1932.

[16] V. C. Rubin and W. K. Ford, "Rotation of the Andromeda nebula from a spectroscopic survey of emission regions," *Astrophysical Journal*, vol. 159, p. 379, 1970.

[17] J. P. Ostriker, P. J. E. Peebles, and A. Yahil, "The size and mass of galaxies, and the mass of the universe," *Astrophysical Journal*, vol. 193, no. 2, pp. L1–L4, 1974.

[18] J. Einasto, A. Kaasik, and E. Saar, "Dynamic evidence on massive coronas of galaxies," *Nature*, vol. 250, no. 5464, pp. 309–310, 1974.

[19] V. C. Rubin, W. K. J. Ford, and N. Thonnard, "Extended rotation curves of high-luminosity spiral galaxies. IV - Systematic dynamical properties, SA through SC," *Astrophysical Journal*, vol. 225, pp. L107–L111, 1978.

[20] A. Bosma, "PhD Thesis 1978: http://ned.ipac.caltech.edu/level5/March05/Bosma/frames.html."

[21] K. Begeman, A. Broeils, and R. Sanders, "Extended rotation curves of spiral galaxies: dark haloes and modified dynamics," *MNRAS*, vol. 249, pp. 523–537, 1991.

[22] D. Walsh, R. Carswell, and R. Weymann, "0957 + 561 A, B: twin quasistellar objects or gravitational lens?" *Nature*, vol. 279, pp. 381–384, 1979.

[23] D. Clowe, M. Bradač, A. H. Gonzalez, M. Markevitch, S. W. Randall, C. Jones, and D. Zaritsky, "A direct empirical proof of the existence of dark matter," *Astrophysical Journal*, vol. 648, no. 2, pp. L109–L113, 2006.

[24] A. Penzias and R. Wilson, "A measurement of excess antenna temperature at 4080 Mc/s," *Astrophysical Journal*, vol. 142, pp. 419–421, 1965.

[25] G. Gamow, "The origin of elements and the separation of galaxies," *Phys. Rev.*, vol. 74, pp. 505–506, 1948.

[26] D. J. Fixsen, E. S. Cheng, J. M. Gales, J. C. Mather, R. A. Shafer, and E. L. Wright, "The cosmic microwave background spectrum from the full COBEFIRAS data set," *Astrophysical Journal*, vol. 473, no. 2, pp. 576–587, 1996.

[27] E. Conklin, "Velocity of the earth with respect to the cosmic background radiation," *Nature*, vol. 222, pp. 971–979, 1969.

[28] P. Henry, "Isotropy of the 3 K background," *Nature*, vol. 231, pp. 516–518, 1971.

[29] R. Sachs and A. Wolfe, "Perturbations of a cosmological model and angular variations of the microwave background," *Astrophysical Journal*, vol. 147, p. 73, 1967.

[30] G. Smoot, C. Bennett, A. Kogut, E. Wright, et al, "Structure in the COBE differential microwave radiometer first-year maps," *Astrophysical Journal Letts.*, vol. 396L, p. L1, 1992.

[31] F. Hoyle, "The synthesis of the elements from hydrogen," *MNRAS*, vol. 106, p. 343, 1946.

[32] R. A. Alpher, H. Bethe, and G. Gamow, "The origin of chemical elements," *Phys. Rev.*, vol. 73, pp. 803–804, 1948.

[33] F. Hoyle, "A new model for the expanding universe," *MNRAS*, vol. 108, p. 372, 1948.

[34] E. M. Burbidge, G. R. Burbidge, W. A. Fowler, and F. Hoyle, "Synthesis of the elements in stars," *Rev. Mod. Phys.*, vol. 29, pp. 547–650, 1957.

[35] F. Hoyle and R. Tayler, "The mystery of the cosmic helium abundance," *Nature*, vol. 203, no. 4950, pp. 1108–1110, 1964.

[36] R. Cooke and M. Fumagalli, "Measurement of the primordial helium abundance from the intergalactic medium," *Nature Astronomy*, vol. 2, pp. 957–961, 2018.

[37] M. Colless, G. Dalton, S. Maddox, and et al, "The 2dF galaxy redshift survey: spectra and redshifts," *MNRAS*, vol. 328, no. 4, pp. 1039–1063, 2001.

[38] M. J. Geller and J. P. Huchra, "Mapping the universe," *Science*, vol. 246, no. 4932, pp. 897–903, 1989.

[39] I. Horvath, J. Hakkila, and Z. Bagoly, "Possible structure in the GRB sky distribution at redshift two," *Astronomy and Astrophysics*, vol. 561, p. L12, 2014.

[40] R. C. Keenan, A. J. Barger, and L. L. Cowie, "Evidence for a 300 Mpc scale under-density in the local galaxy distribution," *Astrophysical Journal*, vol. 775, no. 1, p. 62, 2013.

[41] V. de Lapparent, M. Geller, and J. Huchra, "A slice of the universe," *Astrophysical Journal Letts.*, vol. 302, p. L1, 1986.

[42] P. J. E. Peebles, *Cosmology's Century. An inside history of our modern understanding of the Universe.* Princeton Uni. Press, 2020.

[43] M. Davis, G. Efstathiou, C. Frenk, and S. White, "The evolution of large-scale structure in a universe dominated by cold dark matter," *Astrophysical Journal*, vol. 292, pp. 371–394, 1985.

[44] C. Armendariz-Picon and J. T. Neelakanta, "How cold is cold dark matter?," *Journal of Cosmology and Astroparticle Physics*, vol. 2014, no. 03, pp. 049–049, 2014.

[45] S. Colgate, "Supernovae as a standard candle for cosmology.," *Astrophysical Journal*, vol. 232, pp. 404–408, 1979.

[46] H. U. Norgaard-Nielsen, L. Hansen, H. E. Jorgensen, A. Aragon Salamanca, and R. S. Ellis, "The discovery of a type Ia supernova at a redshift of 0.31," *Nature*, vol. 339, no. 6225, pp. 523–525, 1989.

[47] A. G. Riess, A. V. Filippenko, P. Challis, A. Clocchiatti, A. Diercks, et al, "Observational evidence from supernovae for an accelerating universe and a cosmological constant," *Astronomical Journal*, vol. 116, no. 3, pp. 1009–1038, 1998.

[48] S. Perlmutter, G. Aldering, G. Goldhaber, R. Knop, P. Nugent, et al, and T. S. C. Project, "Measurements of Ω and Λ from 42 high-redshift supernovae," *Astrophysical Journal*, vol. 517, no. 2, pp. 565–586, 1999.

[49] G. Lemaitre, "The beginning of the world from the point of view of quantum theory," *Nature*, vol. 127, p. 706, 1931.

[50] A. G. Riess, L.-G. Strolger, J. Tonry, S. Casertano, H. C. Ferguson, and et al, "Type Ia supernova discoveries at $z > 1$ from the *Hubble* space telescope: Evidence for Past Deceleration and Constraints on Dark Energy Evolution," *Astrophysical Journal*, vol. 607, no. 2, pp. 665–687, 2004.

[51] A. G. Riess, L.-G. Strolger, S. Casertano, H. C. Ferguson, and et al, "New Hubble space telescope discoveries of type Ia supernovae at $z > 1$:

narrowing constraints on the early behavior of dark energy," *Astrophysical Journal*, vol. 659, no. 1, pp. 98–121, 2007.

[52] Planck-Collaboration, "Planck 2015 results - I. Overview of products and scientific results," *Astronomy and Astrophysics*, vol. 594, no. A1, p. 38, 2016.

[53] Planck-Collaboration, "Planck 2013 results. XV. CMB power spectra and likelihood," *Astronomy and Astrophysics*, vol. 571, no. A15, p. 60, 2014.

[54] D. J. Eisenstein, I. Zehavi, D. W. Hogg, and et al, "Detection of the Baryon Acoustic Peak in the Large-Scale Correlation Function of SDSS Luminous Red Galaxies," *Astrophysical Journal*, vol. 633, no. 2, pp. 560–574, 2005.

[55] Planck-Collaboration, N. Aghanim, Y. Akrami, M. Ashdown, and et al, "Planck 2018 results. VI. Cosmological parameters," *arXiv: 1807.06209 [astro-ph.CO]*, 2018.

[56] H. Bondi and T. Gold, "The steady-state theory of the expanding universe," *MNRAS*, vol. 108, p. 252, 1948.

[57] J. Jeans, *Astronomy and Cosmogony*. Cambridge Uni. Press, 1928.

[58] F. Hoyle and J. V. Narlikar, "On the effects of the non-conservation of baryons in cosmology," *Proc. Roy. Soc. A*, vol. 290, pp. 143–161, 1966.

[59] F. Hoyle and J. V. Narlikar, "A radical departure from the 'steady-state' concept in cosmology," *Proc. Roy. Soc. A*, vol. 290, pp. 162–176, 1966.

[60] F. Hoyle, G. Burbidge, and J. V. Narlikar, "A quasi–steady state cosmological model with creation of matter," *Astrophysical Journal*, vol. 410, p. 437, 1993.

[61] F. Hoyle, G. Burbidge, and J. V. Narlikar, *A different approach to cosmology*. Cambridge Uni. Press, 2000.

[62] A. Guth, "Inflationary universe: A possible solution to the horizon and flatness problems," *Phys. Rev. D*, vol. 23, no. 2, p. 15, 1981.

[63] A. Guth, "Inflation," *Proc. Natl. Acad. Sci. USA*, vol. 90, no. 11, pp. 4871–4877, 1993.

[64] A. Linde, "A new inflationary universe scenario: a possible solution of the horizon, flatness, homogeneity, isotropy and primordial monopole problems," *Phys. Letts. B*, vol. 108, no. 6, pp. 389–393, 1982.

[65] A. Albrecht and P. J. Steinhardt, "Cosmology for grand unified theories with radiatively induced symmetry breaking," *Phys. Rev. Lett.*, vol. 48, pp. 1220–1223, 1982.

[66] M. Milgrom, "A modification of the Newtonian dynamics as a possible alternative to the hidden mass hypothesis," *Astrophysical Journal*, vol. 270, pp. 365–370, 1983.

[67] C. Brans and R. H. Dicke, "Mach's principle and a relativistic theory of gravitation," *Phys. Rev.*, vol. 124, p. 925, 1961.

[68] J. D. Bekenstein, "Relativistic gravitation theory for the modified Newtonian dynamics paradigm," *Phys. Rev. D*, vol. 70, p. 083509, 2004.

[69] D. Lovelock, "The Einstein tensor and its generalizations," *Jour. Math. Phys.*, vol. 12, p. 498, 1971.

[70] G. Dvali, G. Gabadadze, and M. Porrati, "4D gravity on a brane in 5D Minkowski space," *Phys. Letts. B*, vol. 485, no. 1, pp. 208–214, 2000.

[71] B. P. Abbott, et al., LIGO Scientific Collaboration, and Virgo Collaboration, "Observation of gravitational waves from a binary black hole merger," *Phys. Rev. Lett.*, vol. 116, no. 6, p. 061102, 2016.

[72] T. Kaluza, "Zum unitatsproblem der physik," *Sitzungsber. Preuss. Akad. Wiss. Berlin.(Math. Phys.)*, vol. 22, p. 966, 1921.

[73] O. Klein, "Elektrodynamik und Wellenmechanik vom Standpunkt des Korrespondenzprinzips," *Z. Physik*, vol. 41, pp. 407–442, 1927.

[74] A. Vilenkin, "Birth of inflationary universes," *Phys. Rev. D*, vol. 27, no. 12, pp. 2848–2855, 1983.

[75] A. Linde, "Eternally existing self-reproducing chaotic inflationary universe," *Phys. Letts. B*, vol. 175, no. 4, pp. 395–400, 1986.

[76] P. J. Steinhardt and N. Turok, "Cosmic evolution in a cyclic universe," *Phys. Rev. D*, vol. 65, p. 126003, 2002.

[77] L. Smolin, *Life of Cosmos*. Oxford Uni. Press, 1997.

[78] G. 't Hooft, "Dimensional reduction in quantum gravity," *arXiV gr-qc/9310026*, 1993.

[79] L. Susskind, "The world as a hologram," *J. Math. Phys.*, vol. 36, no. 11, pp. 6377–6396, 1995.

[80] J. D. Bekenstein, "Universal upper bound on the entropy-to-energy ratio for bounded systems," *Phys. Rev. D*, vol. 23, no. 215, pp. 287–298, 1981.

[81] E. P. Verlinde and K. M. Zurek, "Observational signatures of quantum Gravity in Interferometers," *arXiv gr-qc 1902.08207*, 2019.

[82] A. Vilenkin, "Quantum creation of universes," *Phys. Rev. D*, vol. 30, pp. 509–511, 1984.

[83] S. Tremaine and J. E. Gunn, "Dynamical role of light neutral leptons in cosmology," *Phys. Rev. Letts.*, vol. 42, no. 6, pp. 407–410, 1979.

[84] C. Alcock, R. A. Allsman, D. R. Alves, T. S. Axelrod, A. C. Becker, D. P. Bennett, K. H. Cook, and et al, "The MACHO project: microlensing results from 5.7 years of Large Magellanic Cloud observations," *Astrophysical Journal*, vol. 542, no. 1, pp. 281–307, 2000.

[85] Y. B. Zel'dovich and I. Novikov, "The hypothesis of cores retarded during expansion and the hot cosmological model," *Soviet Astronomy*, vol. 43, p. 758, 1966.

[86] A. A. Aguilar-Arevalo, B. C. Brown, L. Bugel, G. Cheng, and et al, "Significant excess of electronlike events in the MiniBooNE short-baseline neutrino experiment," *Phys. Rev. Lett.*, vol. 121, p. 221801, 2018.

[87] R. D. Peccei and H. R. Quinn, "CP conservation in the presence of Pseudoparticles," *Phys. Rev. Lett.*, vol. 38, pp. 1440–1443, 1977.

[88] R. T. Co and K. Harigaya, "Axiogenesis," *Phys. Rev. Letts.*, vol. 124, no. 11, 2020.

[89] M. Silverman and R. Mallett, "Dark matter as a cosmic Bose-Einstein condensate and possible superfluid," *General Relativity and Gravitation*, vol. 34, pp. 633–649, 2002.

[90] L. Berezhiani and J. Khoury, "Theory of dark matter superfluidity," *Phys. Rev. D*, vol. 92, p. 103510, 2015.

[91] P. J. E. Peebles and B. Ratra, "Cosmology with a time-variable cosmological 'constant'", *Astrophysical Journal Letts.*, vol. 325, pp. L17–L20, 1988.

[92] J. Colin, R. Mohayaee, M. Rameez, and S. Sarkar, "Evidence for anisotropy of cosmic acceleration," *Astronomy and Astrophysics*, vol. 631, p. L13, 2019.

[93] T. Fang, D. A. Buote, P. J. Humphrey, C. R. Canizares, L. Zappacosta, R. Maiolino, G. Tagliaferri, and F. Gastaldello, "Confirmation of X-ray absorption by warm-hot intergalactic medium in the Sculptor wall," *Astrophysical Journal*, vol. 714, no. 2, p. 1715–1724, 2010.

[94] J.-P. Macquart, J. X. Prochaska, M. McQuinn, K. W. Bannister, S. Bhandari, C. K. Day, A. T. Deller, R. D. Ekers, C. W. James, S. O. L. Marnoch, C. Phillips, and D. S. D. Ryder, "A census of baryons in the Universe from localized fast radio bursts," *Nature*, vol. 581, pp. 391–395, 2020.

[95] H. Tanimura, G. Hinshaw, I. G. McCarthy, L. V. Waerbeke, N. Aghanim, Y.-Z. Ma, A. Mead, A. Hojjati, and T. Troster, "A search for warm/hot gas filaments between pairs of SDSS luminous red galaxies," *MNRAS*, vol. 483, pp. 223–234, 2019.

[96] A. de Graaff, Y.-C. Cai, C. Heymans, and J. A. Peacock, "Probing the missing baryons with the Sunyaev-Zel'dovich effect from filaments," *Astronomy and Astrophysics*, vol. 624, p. A48, 2019.

[97] H. Kragh, "'The most philosophical of all the sciences': Karl Popper and physical cosmology: `http://philsci-archive.pitt.edu/9062/1/Popper_\%26_cosmology_PhilSci.pdf`."

[98] K. Migkas, G. Schellenberger, T. H. Reiprich, F. Pacaud, M. E. Ramos-Ceja, and L. Lovisari, "Probing cosmic isotropy with a new X-ray galaxy cluster sample through the L_X-T scaling relation," *Astronomy and Astrophysics*, vol. 636, p. A15, 2020.

[99] J.-P. Petit, "An Interpretation of Cosmological Model with Variable Light Velocity," *Modern Phys. Letts. A*, vol. 3, no. 16, pp. 1527–1532, 1988.

[100] E. Di Valentino, A. Melchiorri, and J. Silk, "Planck evidence for a closed Universe and a possible crisis for cosmology," *Nature Astronomy*, vol. 4, pp. 196–203, 2020.

[101] P. A. M. Dirac, "The quantum theory of the electron," *Proc. R. Soc. Lond. A*, vol. 117, p. 610–624, 1928.

[102] C. D. Anderson, "The apparent existence of easily deflectable positives," *Science*, vol. 76, no. 1967, pp. 238–239, 1932.

[103] A. D. Sakharov, "Violation of CP-invariance, C-asymmetry, and baryon asymmetry of the Universe," *Pisma Zh. Eksp. Teor. Fiz.*, vol. 5, no. 1, pp. 32–35, 1967. [JETP Lett. 5, 24].

[104] J. H. Christenson, J. W. Cronin, V. L. Fitch, and R. Turlay, "Evidence for the 2π decay of the K_2^0 meson," *Phys. Rev. Lett.*, vol. 13, pp. 138–140, 1964.

[105] R. Aaij, C. Abellan Beteta, B. Adeva, M. Adinolfi, and et al, "Observation of CP violation in charm decays," *Phys. Rev. Lett.*, vol. 122, p. 211803, 2019.

[106] G. 't Hooft, "Symmetry breaking through Bell-Jackiw anomalies," *Phys. Rev. Lett.*, vol. 37, pp. 8–11, 1976.

[107] Planck-Collaboration, "Planck 2013 results. XVII. Gravitational lensing by large-scale structure," *Astronomy and Astrophysics*, vol. 571, p. A17, 2014.

[108] C. Heymans, T. Troster, M. Asgari, and et al, "KiDS-1000 cosmology: multi-probe weak gravitational lensing and spectroscopic galaxy clustering constraints," *arXiv:2007.15632 [astro-ph.CO]*, 2020.

[109] A. G. Riess, S. Casertano, W. Yuan, L. M. Macri, and D. Scolnic, "Large Magellanic cloud Cepheid standards provide a 1% foundation for the determination of the Hubble constant and stronger evidence for physics beyond ΛCDM," *Astrophysical Journal*, vol. 876, no. 1, p. 85, 2019.

[110] R. R. Caldwell, M. Kamionkowski, and N. N. Weinberg, "Phantom energy: Dark energy with $w < -1$ causes a cosmic doomsday," *Phys. Rev. Lett.*, vol. 91, p. 071301, 2003.

[111] W. B. Bonnor, "The stability of cosmological models," *Zeitschrift fur Astrophysik*, vol. 35, pp. 10–20, 1954.

[112] P. S. A Ijjas, "A new kind of cyclic universe," *Phys. Letts. B*, vol. 795, no. 10, pp. 666–672, 2019.

[113] R. Penrose, "An outrageous new perspective and its implications for particle physics," *Proceedings of EPAC*, vol. THESPA01, pp. 2759–2762, 2006.

FURTHER READING

Leila Belkora (2002) *Minding the Heavens: The story of our discovery of the Milky Way* Routledge

Bradley Carroll and Dale Ostlie (2017) *An Introduction to Modern Astrophysics* 2nd ed. Cambridge University Press

James Geach (2014) *Galaxy* Reaktion Books

Thomas Kuhn (1962) *The Structure of Scientific Revolutions* republ. 2012 Uni. Chicago Press

James Ladyman (2002) *Understanding Philosophy of Science* Routledge

Andrew Liddle (2015) *An Introduction to Modern Cosmology* John Wiley

Malcolm Longair (2003) *Theoretical Concepts in Physics: An alternative view of theoretical reasoning in physics* 2nd ed. Cambridge University Press

Samir Okasha (2016) *Philosophy of Science: A very short introduction* Oxford Uni. Press

Roger Penrose (2005) *The Road to Reality. A complete guide to the laws of the Universe* Random House

Roger Penrose (2010) *Cycles of Time. An extraordinary new view of the Universe* Random House

Karl Popper (1934) *The logic of scientific discovery* republ. 2002 Routledge

Bertrand Russell (1946) *History of Western Philosophy* republ. 2004 Routledge

Barbara Ryden (2014) *Introduction to Cosmology* Pearson

Peter Schneider (2015) *Extragalactic Astronomy and Cosmology* 2nd ed. Springer-Verlag

Index

Printed in the United States
By Bookmasters